nourish

HOW GOOD FOOD WORKS

FROM SEED TO PLATE

HOW GOOD FOOD WORKS
FROM SEED TO PLATE

Copyright 2021

All proceeds from the sale of this cookbook go to support the Nourish program and its community outreach efforts.

ISBN: 978-0-578-99122-1
Library of Congress number: 2021918779

Published by: Don Sanders

Printed in the United States of America by Bayside Printing Company, Inc.

To order additional copies: www.howgoodfoodworkscookbook.org

Authors: Laura S. Moore, John Wesley McWhorter and Joseph R. Novak
Book production manager, research and writing: Roni Atnipp
Cover and layout design: Elise DeSilva – Limb Design (www.limbdesign.com)
Editing: Doug Williams
Recipe development: John Wesley McWhorter
Food photography: Debora Smail (www.deborasmail.com)
Food stylist: Chef Omar Pereney (www.culinarymatters.com)
Location and portrait photography: Alexander's Fine Portrait Design (www.alexanderportraits.com)

UTHealth School of Public Health - Houston
Michael & Susan Dell Center for Healthy Living
Nourish Program
1200 Pressler Street
Houston, TX 77030
713-500-9347
www.nourishprogram.org

In the making of this book, every attempt has been made to verify names and facts. We apologize if any errors have been made.

For more information: www.howgoodfoodworks.org

Dedication

To all communities with the hope of living healthier lives.

Table of Contents

Nourish is founded on a basic belief:

By improving people's understanding of food – how it's grown, harvested, prepared and seasoned – we can show how easy it is to eat healthy and live a healthier lifestyle.

Since 2012, when our vision began to take shape, the Nourish program has become a focal point for nutrition education in the Texas Medical Center. By providing students, healthcare professionals and members of the community with critical culinary skills and knowledge, we are training them on how good food works. But beyond that, we're helping them address and prevent a range of health issues that are the result of poor nutrition.

Our journey started somewhat humbly, in a small room with a few tables and vending machines. With the help of enlightened leadership at the UTHealth School of Public Health–Houston, the generosity of our donors and the commitment of our faculty, staff and students, we have grown significantly in terms of our offerings and reach. Today, no other course of study in the country can compare to Nourish.

Over the years, it has been thrilling to see how everyone involved has completely embraced the program and recognized its benefits. We have broadened the understanding and appreciation of food and strengthened the connection between who people are and what they consume. In many ways, we have transformed eating from a daily act to a lifelong experience. In doing so, we have made communities and their members healthier and stronger.

This book tells the story of how Nourish accomplished all that. We hope you enjoy it and see just how good food works and leads us to healthier lives.

Laura Moore was a bit surprised.

When she arrived at UTHealth School of Public Health – Houston in 2012 and worked as the director of its Dietetic Internship Program, she quickly learned that the students in her cohort didn't know much about food – where it came from or how to make it taste good. She had hoped they were getting that kind of instruction as undergraduates.

"We had an advanced medical nutrition curriculum and a 1,200-hour external supervised practicum – both of which were outstanding – but we weren't teaching them anything that was specifically food-related," she said. "They were working on their Master of Public Health degree and would be Registered Dietitian Nutritionists after they graduated, but I realized they didn't have the tools they needed to teach people about food and how food contributes to healthier lives. So I decided at that point we needed to make some changes."

Moore was well-prepared for the role of a change agent, as food has always been "first and foremost in my life." A Registered Dietitian Nutritionist with formal training from L'Academie de Cuisine and Le Cordon Bleu, she had worked in the hospitality industry for years before becoming the food service manager at Memorial Hermann Hospital and a visiting assistant professor at the University of Houston.

Moore knew there would be challenges raising operating funds for the soon to be Nourish program. Grant funding is unpredictable and the application process is extremely time-consuming; it can sometimes take a year or longer to apply for and receive funding. "I knew that any grant we received would be relatively small given the size of the program and then it would run out." My colleagues Drs. Deanna Hoelscher and Shreela Sharma were very supportive of Nourish and on board to help apply for grant funding for community interventions; however, the day-to-day operations of the program would be up to her. She knew she would need additional help. Enter Don Sanders.

Don Sanders was no stranger to risk.

He founded Sanders Morris Harris, a leading financial management firm, a month after the 1987 stock market crash, a time when institutional investors were being battered amid the world's first contemporary financial crisis. But when his wife, Laura, came to him with an idea of a program that would basically raise the food IQ of her students, he didn't see any risk – he just saw the rewards.

"I've been fortunate in my life from a business standpoint and to have enough money to live the life we want to live and to still help others," he said. "But when I donate, I want to, first of all, be able to see, in tangible terms, where the money goes. Next, I want to see the impact it will have now. And finally, I want to know that five or ten years from now, it will still be where it is today – or better."

Nourish checked all those boxes.

Moore's ambitions were lofty. She wanted facilities that could provide her students with hands-on training on how good food works: a garden, so they could see where food came from and how to harvest it; a teaching kitchen, where they could learn to prepare and cook food; and a clinical simulation lab, where they could learn to manage food-related medical conditions and talk to patients about how to improve their nutrition habits.

After roughly two years of negotiating for space at the UTHealth School of Public Health in the Texas Medical Center, work on the first phase of Moore's dream, a holistic garden, began in 2014. She turned to Dr. Joe Novak, a noted horticulturist who earned his PhD in vegetable crops with a minor in plant pathology and international agriculture at Cornell University. After teaching stints at Texas A&M and Louisiana State, he almost retired in 2011. His retirement didn't last long.

> After roughly two years of negotiating for space at the UTHealth School of Public Health in the Texas Medical Center, work on the first phase of Moore's dream, a holistic garden, began in 2014.

An ideal choice for the garden

"I wasn't ready to retire," said Novak, "so I taught at Rice University for a couple of years. Then, one day, Laura called out of nowhere and asked if I wanted to create a garden. So I created a garden."

Novak was an ideal choice. His area of research was sociohorticulture, whose theoretical focus is the relationship between people and plants and how that relationship can be used to bring about positive changes in the lives of certain populations. It fit well with Moore's hope that Nourish could serve as a vital resource for improving health in underserved communities.

Construction of the garden began in 2014, and by 2015, students were getting the hands-on experience Moore wanted. It provided a natural setting for instruction on how gardens and gardening lead to better nutrition and mental health, prevent or reduce a range of chronic conditions and enhance physical activity.

The education was practical as well. "We teach how and when to plant, how to harvest, whether to use seeds or transplants, how to take care of the soil, pest management, how to select crops for each spring, summer and fall," Novak said. "It's everything – how gardening is done right."

But there was one small problem.

"We had this nice, lovely garden," Moore said, "except there was no money to operate it. We hadn't written any grants."

"I looked at Laura," Sanders said, "and asked, 'What do you plan to do?' I think there was a sense right at that moment that the garden was just going to go away, wither up and die."

Problem solved

Sanders was already planning on giving "a little bit" to support Nourish. But when it became clear that the garden, to say nothing of the rest of Moore's larger blueprint for the entire program, needed more help, Sanders stepped up and provided the necessary seed money.

He and Moore donated $1 million, matched by UTHealth as part of the university's Game Changer Initiative, that was dedicated to operating the facilities. They also donated another $790,000 toward a $1.5 million build-out, and the UTHealth School of Public Health contributed the rest.

Moore said the support of Dr. Eric Boerwinkle, dean of UTHealth School of Public Health, was crucial then – and remains so now.

"Eric was instrumental in helping us through," she said. "He's a wonderful person and has been a strong advocate. It's amazing the impact he's had on the school, the visibility of the school, the students and the community. We now have the only School of Public Health in the country that has this kind of program, and our internship program is one of a few Master of Public Health – Registered Dietitian Nutritionists programs."

Sanders, in typical fashion, shrugged off his role: "So, I think, everything worked out pretty well."

From garden to kitchen

The 5,000-square-foot holistic garden was just one pillar in the Nourish foundation.

"We started the garden, where the food came from," Moore said, "and then wanted to take that harvest into the kitchen, where we could teach students how to cook and make healthy food taste better."

Moore had redesigned the kitchen at the University of Houston, but its focus was commercial. For Nourish, she had other ideas.

"A lot of teaching kitchens are created and set up like that," she explained. "I wanted ours to be more like a home kitchen, something practical. Maybe a little more upscale and innovative, but still a place that enabled students to work and learn and cook in a setting that was more familiar to them and to the communities they will eventually serve."

But achieving that was not without challenges.

She needed a space that was highly visible, somewhere students could easily find and access, making learning more convenient. To her, that meant the first-floor lobby of the university's UTHealth School of Public Health – Houston building. What she got was something else entirely.

"That just was not doable."

The only available space that was not for classroom use was a vending room. "It had machines for soft drinks and candy and a couple of tables," Sanders said. "It was full of things that people who maintain a healthy lifestyle don't eat. It was going to be a big leap to get where Laura wanted to go."

Then came the next obstacle. "We were set to move ahead with reconfiguring that room when the decision was made to put us in the basement," Moore said. "That just was not doable."

What followed were discussions among Moore, Sanders, dean Boerwinkle and Deanna Hoelscher, regional dean of UTHealth School of Public Health – Austin and director of the Michael & Susan Dell Center for Healthy Living, which oversees the program. They pitched to Boerwinkle on how they wanted the kitchen to look, where it needed to be and how that affected what they wanted to do. He agreed, and the project moved forward, with Sanders committing to shouldering half the cost.

With the green light from Boerwinkle, Moore became deeply involved in developing the Research and Teaching Kitchen. Equipped with double ovens, induction cooktop, refrigerators and freezers, it gives dietetic interns a facility where faculty can provide instruction on healthy cooking techniques and medical nutrition therapy education for diet-related diseases and medical conditions.

A team of Registered Dietitian Nutritionists work in rotation, creating recipes under the supervision of Moore and John "Wesley" McWhorter. McWhorter is the Director of Culinary Nutrition at Nourish; he teaches most of the culinary medicine classes and is the leader of the culinary medicine curriculum.

Besides the appliances, the kitchen – also a training ground for school educators – is equipped with 4 cameras, production-quality lighting and an 80-inch monitor.

"On the one hand, the technology allows participants to see the preparation practices up close," Moore said. "On the other, it allows us to stream live so we can reach not only one clinic but several at once, sharing more of our resources to more of the community."

Underscoring that, Nourish has created a virtual toolkit that includes the program's cooking videos, animated nutritional videos and other online instructions on how to eat better and cook healthier.

While Moore said the goal of the teaching kitchen was culinary education, it has other aims as well.

"We also wanted to give students the confidence that comes with practicing and understanding how to cook," she explained. "We want them to know how to release flavors in food, and enjoy it. We also want them to understand the connection between food and culture."

Overcoming a challenge in the kitchen

Moore conceded that it's sometimes a challenge to convince skeptics that "healthy" food can be flavorful and that there are good-tasting, highly nutritional substitutes for foods that might not be in their best dietary interests. "We're overcoming that challenge in the kitchen," she said.

As an example, Moore cited how a traditional burger can be easily transformed into a healthier version without sacrificing texture or taste: "We start with 90/10 beef and replace half the beef with finely chopped mushrooms and black beans. Add Worcestershire sauce and grill seasonings for a more umami flavor. It looks and tastes amazing and it's healthier."

McWhorter said that the kitchen, in combination with the holistic garden, was what first attracted him to UTHealth.

"In 2014 to 2015, when it was starting to take off, not many places had a garden or chefs and Registered Dietitian Nutritionists," he said. "Not everyone saw the benefits. It was a time when everyone thought the idea of 'healthy cooking' was crazy."

"I would be speaking, and I'd ask the audience what food they associate with healthy eating. Often, the answer was salad. We're proving that there are enjoyable alternatives that taste good, and that's what people want. They don't care what's better for them or what's necessarily healthy. They only care that it tastes good.

"That's what we're teaching."

Meet Mr. Sims

So Nourish had a garden to grow good food and a kitchen to prepare it right. The next and final step was to take the lessons learned in those two facilities and translate them into a setting where students could apply and learn skills that are central to managing nutrition-related medical issues and diseases.

Thus, Mr. Sims was born.

He's controlled by Jeanne Piga-Plunkett, lead clinical instructor. Mr. Sims is a lifelike 3G manikin – essentially a robot – that is a "patient" in Nourish's Simulation and Clinical Assessment Lab. Instructors can get him to exhibit multiple characteristics that students are likely to find in actual patients: symptoms, everything from sweating, to sounding like he's about to throw up, to suffering cardiac arrest.

"What we're doing," Moore said, "is mimicking chronic conditions that can be related to poor dietary habits – cardiovascular disease, obesity and type 2 diabetes, for example – and then having students 'talk' to Mr. Sims about how those issues can be addressed and managed through improved nutrition.

"The benefits are huge. They learn how to effectively consult with patients and how to assess them physically. But from the larger perspective, they learn how to talk to patients about food in ways that connect with people."

To Moore, this final point, "talking about food," is a key principle of Nourish's mission.

"As a Registered Dietitian Nutritionist, in the early stages of my practice, I'd be talking to patients, and suddenly I realized I didn't know how to do it," she said. "I had a lot of experience with food, and I had a good understanding of food, but at the time, I didn't really know how to make that knowledge relevant to people who really needed to hear it."

One of the problems, she believed, was context.

"You can talk to patients about calories, proteins, carbohydrates and other nutrients, all of the basics," she continued. "But it doesn't work that way. They don't understand. They're not interested in what a good carb or a bad carb is. They look at a restaurant menu and see how many calories are in the items, and they don't really care."

Echoing McWhorter, she added: "What they care about is whether it tastes good. So that's what we're teaching in the simulation lab: how to talk to patients in practical and culturally appropriate food terms rather than nutrient numbers. We teach them to talk about seasoning; for example, this is how you can make okra and green beans taste good, this is how you can replace white rice with cauliflower rice – and we do it in non-clinical language that makes sense."

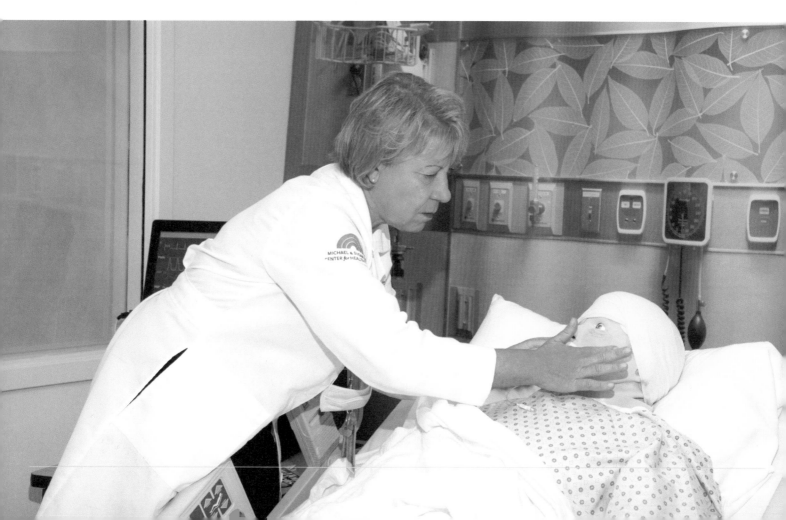

Then the program really took off

In January 2016, the UTHealth Development Office held a fundraising luncheon on behalf of Nourish. While the event was successful, the program still needed more operating capital, so Sanders decided to donate $1 million, provided the university would match the gift. It did, and on November 16, 2016, UTHealth officially unveiled the Nourish program's seed to plate facilities – the holistic garden, the teaching kitchen and the clinical simulation lab.

"These resources will allow us to develop innovative research, teaching and practice programs to help us improve the population health of Texas," said Boerwinkle, the dean of UTHealth School of Public Health, at the ribbon-cutting ceremony. "Nutrition-related diseases – such as obesity, type 2 diabetes, cardiovascular disease and cancer – are significant public health issues, especially here in the state of Texas.

"Many of these can be addressed through nutrition, but unfortunately, people don't know how to prepare healthy foods. In fact, a lot of people don't know where healthy foods come from. They think green beans are grown in a can. I encourage everyone to go to the garden to see a real green bean."

125 sign-ups for 20 slots

While Boerwinkle's encouragement came in 2016, students had, in fact, been coming to Nourish more than a year before the facilities formally opened.

In 2016, after the construction was completed, the program began offering volunteer classes in culinary medicine at no cost to medical students who wanted to attend. They could enroll through a link online. Within 15 minutes, more than 125 students signed up for the 20 available slots.

"We didn't expect that kind of response," Moore said. "It was like, 'Wow, we've really got something here. Thank you.'

"But I was also thrilled to know that there were students who really wanted to learn how to better themselves and their health. That's one of the great advantages of Nourish: Once students take the course, they learn how to take care of their own health and can then pass that along to their patients."

"Then the program really took off." Moore said. "It moved into the medical, nursing and dental schools – so we picked up all three UTHealth professional schools, brought them all in, took them out to the garden and showed them how to cook. It was culinary medicine, and we were helping them to help people become healthier through food."

Success begets success, and it wasn't long before the program, at long last, began to attract grant money. The first award eventually allowed Moore to take the program where she'd always wanted it to go.

Delivering the good food message

Moore, Sanders, McWhorter and Novak all shared a belief that good food works for the community.

McWhorter has spoken and written frequently about the societal impacts of good nutrition. Novak's concept of sociohorticulture holds that gardens can build neighborhoods. Moore started Nourish to "make our community and other communities healthier and provide an easier, better way to talk about food." Sanders had earned respect as a community leader for decades through his charitable donations and provided seed money for Brighter Bites, a non-profit that delivers fresh fruit and vegetables directly to families.

With that collective pedigree, it's no surprise that at some point, Nourish's healthy eating message would eventually be delivered directly to those who could benefit most from it. Expansion required funds, however, and grants had been tough to win. But eventually, one came in from a foundation in Michigan that moved the program out of the Texas Medical Center and into the community.

The award in 2017 was from the Allen Foundation, and it targeted two areas of Houston. It was designed to "improve dietary intake in diverse, low-income areas" by providing nutrition education through a culinary arts program. Secondarily, it aimed to build a capability in community centers that trained local health workers to broaden the program's instruction and model good nutritional behavior.

"The ability to go in and truly help people by showing them how good food works for them to improve their dietary habits, health and lifestyles – that's what the program is really about," she added.

A family affair

"It was exciting," Moore said of the grant. "We had trained our students, we had our dietetic interns and our medical students working with us, and now we had the financial support to take nutritional education into the field. From there, it was like, 'Here we go. This is what we've been waiting for.'"

Award funds in hand, the Nourish team would come into local clinics with their portable teaching kitchen and run classes right in the clinic's lobby.

It was truly a family affair.

"We had families with children, so we provided childcare," Moore said. "We had a child who was a cardiac patient, others who were obese, as well as some diabetic patients. It was a mixed group of people, but they enjoyed just being there, learning to cook as a family and sharing ideas about food, culture and what they cook. It was heartwarming."

More grants followed, and Nourish developed a "train the trainer" model in which dietetic interns and medical students were instructed on how to go into neighborhoods and community centers and teach residents how to prepare and cook healthy, good-tasting foods. Additionally, they trained clinic staff how to implement the Nourish model, a strategy that Moore said keeps the program sustainable.

"The ability to go in and truly help people by showing them how good food works for them to improve their dietary habits, health and lifestyles – that's what the program is really about," she added.

In the end, perseverance pays off

To Sanders, the ultimate success of Nourish lies in creating a "win" for students and the people who benefit from the program. "I mean, if it doesn't help others," he asked, "what have you achieved? But if you look at all we've accomplished, it's clear we are doing what we set out to do."

He was also quick to point out that Moore's perseverance played no small part in Nourish's emergence as a one-of-a-kind resource.

"There was some push and shove from time to time, some debates over what to do, but Laura kept standing up for what she believed in. You have to give her the credit for getting everything done."

Moore didn't necessarily take credit, but she did affirm Sanders' remarks about her commitment.

"I've never been one to give up," she said. "I've been told so many times, 'No, you can't do this,' instead I stayed the course. I kept saying, 'This is what we're going to do, this is what we need to do and this is how we're going to do it.' This is our vision and mission — to take care of underserved communities."

"We are a public health focused community outreach program. We have an obligation to be out there, among the public, helping people get better, live better and be healthier. That's why we're here."

"This is what we're going to do, this is what we need to do and this is how we're going to do it. This is our vision and mission — to take care of underserved communities."

JOHN "WESLEY" MCWHORTER

DrPH MS, RDN, LD, CSCS
ASSISTANT PROFESSOR, HEALTH PROMOTION AND BEHAVIORAL SCIENCES
DIRECTOR OF CULINARY NUTRITION, NOURISH PROGRAM

"The problem with nutrition is that we treat healthy eating as punishment – removing enjoyment and pleasure from the table. Anyone who has been on a diet knows that's not sustainable in the long run".

Wesley McWhorter learned at an early age that eating food that was good for you didn't always translate to food that tasted good.

Raised in South Alabama, McWhorter – the Director of Culinary Nutrition for the Nourish program – grew up in a family with a history of health conditions that included diabetes, and cardiac disease. His grandfather had a heart attack when McWhorter was in his early teens and then tried a heart-healthy diet.

"It didn't work," McWhorter recalled. "My grandfather said, 'This is gross. I'm not going to eat it.'" Thus began a journey that led him to culinary school right out of high school and eventually to the UTHealth School of Public Health, where he is an assistant professor in health promotion and behavioral sciences.

As he began to move up the ladder from dishwasher to private chef to educator, McWhorter's view of healthy eating began to expand – and it went beyond the issue of taste alone.

"Nutrition tends to be elitist," he said, "something for only those who are well-off. There are stereotypes too. People look at Southern food, for example, and automatically assume it's unhealthy. That doesn't respect the culture of the food." (Unsurprisingly, he once gave a presentation titled *The Southern Plate – Inclusive Delicious Meals*).

"We all have our favorite foods," he continued. "We've grown up with certain foods. We taste and enjoy food differently. Flavor is extremely personal, and flavor shapes what you like. As I continued my studies, from culinary school through my doctoral work, it became clearer to me that food isn't bad, but healthy food is better. So the challenge became, how do you make healthy food taste better?"

One key, he said, is not to make exposure to healthy eating a negative experience. Forcing people to eat something they don't like probably won't make anyone shift to a better diet.

But he's also a realist, which has informed his views on preparing healthy food.

"You can't create a dish that everyone loves," he said, "and I understand that. If someone doesn't like something, it's okay. You don't demand that they eat it because it's good for them. We ask why you don't like it. Maybe we can cook it differently, or season it differently, and if that doesn't work, we try something else."

He also recognizes that no one wants to be sick, and that patients who resist the idea of healthy eating may be struggling with other issues.

"Our work – nutrition-based training of Registered Dietitian Nutritionists, to culinary medicine, to food prescription programs – is to remove as many of these barriers as possible, and to identify and address systemic issues that can negatively affect good nutrition."

At the end of the day, McWhorter pursues his good-taste goals without judging or preaching. He simply wants to democratize healthy eating, and provide everyone with the opportunity to embrace their food culture and enjoy their food.

"We're not trying to be prescriptive," he added. "We're not saying you're at fault if you're eating unhealthy. We're saying here's how you can prepare good food to taste good – how you can still get the flavors you enjoy, just in a healthier way, so that it becomes a sustainable lifestyle for you and your family."

HOW GOOD FOOD WORKS IN THE GARDEN

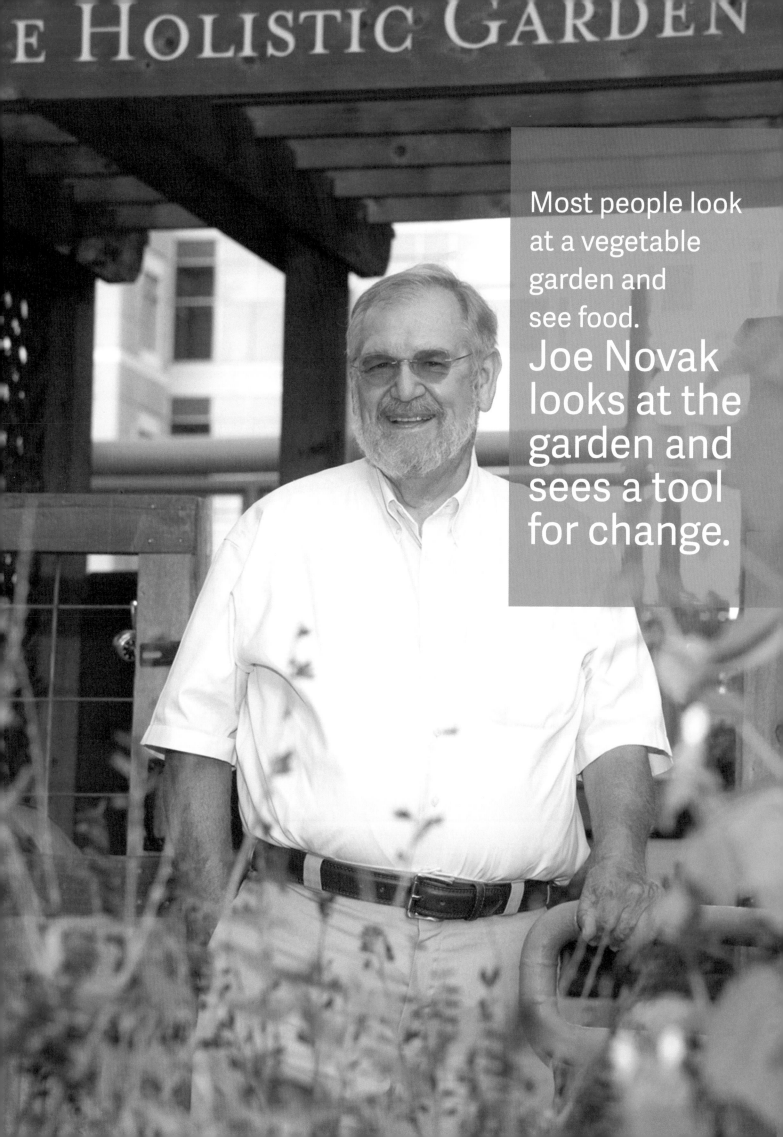

E HOLISTIC GARDEN

Most people look at a vegetable garden and see food. Joe Novak looks at the garden and sees a tool for change.

> "When you look at people who live to be 100, they tend to be physically active, consume a Mediterranean-focused diet and are socially connected," he said. "And then you think, 'Aha, they're gardeners.' So we try to design gardens that let people do it themselves."

Novak, who designed the Nourish program's holistic garden, coined the term "sociohorticulture" in 1971, describing it as the study of plants from a social context – the intersection of plants and people. "Human contact with gardens and nature can deliver a lot of societal benefits to individuals, special needs populations, neighborhoods and communities," he said.

"He grew up on a small farm in Ohio where he loved contact with nature. A two-year stay in the Philippines as a graduate exchange student helped him realize that American agriculture had lost contact with nature."

Novak had been focusing much of his educational pursuits on how to improve the many ways plants were grown. Watching Filipino farmers, he saw the link between their work and how they approached their lives. "They were poor, but they were in touch with nature and their surroundings," he said. "Watching them, I couldn't help but think we were losing that connection in the United States."

After teaching at Louisiana State, Texas A&M and Rice University, Novak got the opportunity to build a garden for the UTHealth School of Public Health, where he is an adjunct professor. He started from a simple premise: Gardening should be available to everyone.

"We wanted anyone to be able to use it, and that meant making it accessible for people with special needs – people in wheelchairs or using prosthetics, older adults, those suffering from PTSD," he said. "The Nourish program holistic garden is an ideal demonstration project because it shows how that can be done."

The role of gardening in good mental and physical health is at the core of Novak's belief that plants and lifestyle are inextricably woven.

"Once people start growing good food, they start eating good food. And they tend to live longer, with fewer major health problems."

"Nature is restorative," he explained. "It calms us and makes us happier, reduces anxiety and makes us less depressed. Getting people outside is great therapy. It's just fun."

For all of those benefits, however, Novak is steadfast in his belief that gardens should be community-centered.

"You have to look at a neighborhood, determine what it needs and then design a garden based on those needs," he said. "If you do that, if you are purposeful, you'll see tangible results. People will come together, work together and enjoy the experience."

That also underscores what and how he teaches: "I tell my students that they have an obligation to share the rewards of their education with those who are less fortunate. I want them to understand that they can use what they learn about horticulture to improve communities and help the people – all of the people – who live in them."

The Food Garden

Written by Joe Novak

Few things are as delicious and nutritious as vegetables, fruits and herbs fresh from your garden. Growing your own produce is a healthy form of exercise, keeps your brain active and keeps you in touch with nature. Research shows that gardeners have fewer major chronic disorders than the population as a whole and tend to live longer. If you are cooking at home using produce grown organically in your home garden, it is free of pesticides and tastes better too.

What to Grow

What to grow is a decision that all gardeners have to make. Base your crop choices on what you like to eat, what is healthier for you and tastes better when harvested fresh from your own garden, and how much room you have for growing crops.

Choosing the right variety of a crop can make the difference between success and failure. Always check reliable sources to find the varieties recommended for your area. Many crops exist in both open-pollinated and hybrid forms. Hybrid varieties tend to have many advantages, but their seeds are usually more expensive. Using hybrids often warrants producing transplants, since seeding directly in the garden takes much more seed to achieve a good stand.

Colorful vegetables tend to be more nutritious and have more medicinal value than white or light-colored vegetables. Plant breeding is producing many vegetables in a wide array of colors, often every color of the rainbow.

When to Grow

In cooler parts of the country, tomatoes are grown and harvested from July through September, but in the warmer parts, tomato fruits are ripe in June and July and no longer available in August and September.

Frost dates are a major factor in growing any vegetable. Vegetable crops are divided into cool-season crops that are frost tolerant and warm-season crops that cannot tolerate frost. Cabbage, spinach, lettuce, broccoli, kale, carrots, sugar snap peas, parsley and chives are frost-tolerant crops and can be grown better in the cooler months of the year. Tomatoes, peppers, squash, cucumbers, beans, corn and basil are warm-season crops that are grown during the frost-free months of the year.

Some crops need specific conditions to form heads, bulbs or tubers. For example, cabbage plants form flowers when exposed repeatedly to cold temperatures but form heads in milder weather. Onions and garlic need long days to form bulbs, and Irish potatoes need intermediate to long days to form tubers. Cucumber and squash plants produce female flowers and, therefore, fruits later when temperatures are hot but earlier at warm temperatures. Green beans do not bear fruit in hot weather.

The number of days from seed to harvest is a common estimate of the length of time that it will take to produce a crop. Crops grown in long days in summer in northern parts of the country grow faster than crops grown in short days in winter in the south. At the same day length, a crop in cool temperatures will grow slower than a crop growing at higher temperatures.

Always check local sources to know the planting date for a crop.

The number of days from seed to harvest is a common estimate of the length of time that it will take to produce a crop. Crops grown in long days in summer in northern parts of the country grow faster than crops grown in short days in winter in the south.

Soil Preparation

Vegetables and herbs grow best in soils that have almost equal amounts of sand, silt and clay particles, called loamy soils. Soil preparation should begin by turning under existing organic matter, loosening the soil and shaping the planting beds. In areas of higher rainfall, the plant beds are raised 8–12 inches above the level of the furrows (trenches) that provide drainage, but in areas that are not as wet, the crops can be grown on the flat soil surface. If seeds are to be sown (planted) to start the crop in the garden, the seed bed needs more thorough preparation than the rest of the soil would need. Also, if transplants, bulbs or tubers are to be planted, less soil preparation is needed than when sowing seeds. Remember, overworking the soil can be as bad as not working it enough.

Fertilization

Fertilizers are often applied when the soil is being prepared. If you use organic fertilizer, pellets can be spread over the soil surface and lightly worked into the soil. Inorganic fertilizers are salts, for example, ammonium, sulfate and nitrate and if you are not careful, they can damage the crops. They are usually applied during planting and a few inches away from the seeds that are to be sown or plants that are to be set in the garden.

Nitrogen, phosphorus and potassium are the three major nutrients that are applied. Nitrogen promotes growth of the leaves and stems, but too much nitrogen can delay the development of flowers, fruits and seeds and can lead to poor-quality roots and tubers. All crops usually need nitrogen, but leafy crops, such as lettuce, spinach, kale and basil, suffer more when they are nitrogen deficient. Phosphorus promotes the development of roots, flowers, fruits and seeds. Phosphorus-deficient plants that are grown for flowers, fruits and seeds don't produce well. All plants need potassium, which lines all membranes of the cells. Crops that suffer from a deficiency of potassium are those that produce large organs, such as thick stems, fleshy roots, tubers and bulbs.

Compost can be used as fertilizer if it is rich in nutrients and has a carbon-to-nitrogen ratio of 24:1 or narrower. The most effective way to use compost as a fertilizer is to apply it as a blanket about 2 inches deep over the effective root zone of the plant. The effective root zone usually extends 1–2 feet from the base of the plant.

Soil preparation should begin by turning under existing organic matter, loosening the soil and shaping the planting beds.

Planting the Crop

Most vegetables are planted from seeds. Seeds can either be sown directly in the garden soil or used to grow transplants. Some exceptions are garlic, which is grown by planting garlic bulbs; Irish potatoes, which are grown by planting potato tubers; and sweet potatoes, which are grown from transplants produced from sweet potato roots. Mustard, spinach, carrots, beets, radishes, lettuce, beans, peas, corn, cucumbers and squash are examples of crops that are commonly seeded directly in garden soil.

Germination of most garden seeds takes 5–10 days, but a few crops may take longer. After the plants are established, it is important to thin them for proper spacing.

The sowing depth is critical. Seeds of vegetable crops should be sown to a depth two to four times the thickness of the seeds. Planting too deep or too shallow will result in poor germination.

A very successful technique when sowing seeds is to create a shallow furrow for the seeds, saturate it with water, sow seeds on the surface of the saturated soil and then pull dry soil over the top to the effective depth. Firm (cover) the soil over the position of the sown seeds. Do not water again until the seedlings come up.

Tomatoes, eggplant, peppers, cabbage, broccoli, cauliflower and kale are crops that are commonly transplanted to the garden. Transplants can be purchased at garden centers or grown by a gardener. It is important to set most transplants in a garden at the same depth that the plant is grown or produced in its container. The exception is tomatoes, which are often set a few inches deeper because they send roots out of the base of their stems.

The planting date is usually determined by whether the crop is a cool-season crop (meaning it can tolerate frost) or a warm-season one (and can't tolerate a frost). Another factor is soil temperature. Cool-season crops are usually planted while the soil is cool, but warm-season crops should only be planted after the soil has warmed.

Spacing

Spacing between plants is very important. Greens and root crops can be sown a few seeds per inch in a row and then thinned to 2 or more inches apart. Beans and peas are planted a few seeds per foot of row. Potatoes, sweet potatoes, okra and corn are planted a foot apart. Tomatoes, summer squash, cucumbers and melons are planted 2–3 feet apart, and watermelons, pumpkins and winter squash are planted as much as 6–8 feet apart.

As a general rule, the wider the spacing, the larger the plant will become and the larger the harvested product will be. Setting Irish potatoes more than 1 foot apart results in larger potatoes. Broccoli plants set 3 inches apart will form heads, but they will be much smaller than those set 12 or 15 inches apart.

Water Management

All food crops need good drainage. If excess water cannot drain from the soil, the roots will not grow well or will rot and the crop will not produce. Tomatoes, peppers, Irish potatoes, beans, peas and cucurbits are among the most sensitive to water-logged soil.

All food crops need irrigation; most need 1–2 inches of water per week. Without irrigation, the yield will be low and many crops will produce fruits or roots with splits in them. When possible, drip irrigation is the best form of irrigation for the food garden because it is efficient, easy to use and thorough. Spray and furrow irrigation can also be used, but results are often not as good as with drip irrigation.

Mulches

Most food gardens benefit from the use of mulch. A mulch can be a particle mulch of grass clippings, pine straw, old tree leaves or compost applied in a 3–6 inch deep blanket over the top of the effective root zone of the plant, or it can be a sheet of plastic, cardboard or other product produced for the purpose. Mulches reduce water evaporation and control weeds; some also add nutrients to the next crop that is to be grown in the area.

Weed Control

Weeds are plants that grow where they're not wanted. Weeds rob garden plants of light, water and nutrients and can harbor pathogens, pests and other undesirable organisms. Weed control is usually done mechanically by hoeing, pulling manually or mulching.

Pest Management

Some insect pests do damage by chewing holes in the plant. Other insects and mites suck sap out of the plants and inject toxins. Most insects and mites also spread pathogens and make wounds that allow pathogens to get into the plant. The gardener must make the decision as to whether the pest is doing enough damage to warrant control or not.

Common controls include mechanically removing the pest from the plant or garden, using organic or nonorganic pesticides and maintaining a healthy ecosystem with beneficial organisms that destroy the pests, for example, toads, birds and beneficial insects.

Disease Management

A disease is an abnormal condition in a plant. Physiogenic diseases are caused by the environment, for example, frost damage, sun scald and hard freezes. These problems are usually controlled by the planting date and by barriers and other mechanical means. Pathogenic diseases are caused by microbes. They can be controlled by the use of resistant varieties, exclusion, sanitation and other nonchemical methods, or through some chemicals. In all cases, a healthy plant has a better chance of surviving an attack and warding off a pathogen.

Beneficial Organisms in the Garden Ecosystem

The garden is an ecosystem with many good and bad organisms. Examples of good organisms are microbes in the soil and air, earthworms, lady bugs and other predatory insects, spiders, bees and other pollinators, birds, toads, frogs, snakes and other reptiles. Destructive organisms or pests include weeds, chewing and sucking insects, mites, pathogens, squirrels and other mammals. Some members of the ecosystem fit both categories, and many are neutral. The role of the gardener is to determine which destructive organisms warrant control strategies and which can simply be ignored.

Harvesting and Handling the Produce

One of the biggest mistakes gardeners make is not harvesting a crop when it is ready for harvest. Harvesting at the right stage not only gives better quality produce but also helps avoid various other problems, such as attacks by pests and pathogens. For example, a bird pecking into a ripe tomato is doing what is natural. The gardener can avoid this problem by picking tomatoes when they are still turning and finishing the ripening process indoors.

Newly harvested produce must be handled carefully. It is tender, often brittle and easily damaged.

When the plant is finished producing, the last step in managing the garden is getting rid of any plant debris. Leaving plant debris in the garden allows pests and pathogens to survive until your next garden season.

Harvesting at the right stage not only gives better quality produce but also helps avoid various other problems, such as attacks by pests and pathogens.

HOW GOOD FOOD WORKS IN THE KITCHEN

Vegetable Roasting Guidelines and Tips

Basic Instructions:

Roasting/baking pan
The pan should have low sides (2½ inches or lower) but long enough to hold your vegetables in a single layer with space around each veggie.

Parchment paper
Cover the bottom of the pan with one sheet of parchment paper. Use it only at a roasting temperature below 450°, or the paper may catch fire. Use tin foil at higher temperatures.

Vegetable size
Vegetables should be cut in similar sizes to cook them at the same rate. Cook similar vegetables together or cook in batches.

Formula for oil and seasonings
The ratio is 1 pound vegetables to 2 tablespoons oil to 1 tablespoon seasonings. Oil should give the vegetables a shiny appearance. Toss to cover all vegetables with oil evenly. Oil should have a high smoke point (olive, canola, avocado).

Oven temperature
Preheat the oven to the desired temperature. We recommend 400° conventional for most vegetables, but roasting at higher or lower temperatures is fine. However, cooking time will need to be adjusted.

Ready?
When are vegetables ready? Roast vegetables until fork-tender. They should have a golden-brown appearance.

Veggie Fruits and Fruits
400° for 15–20 minutes
Season with salt after cooking.

Eggplants	Delicata	Squash:
Peppers	Kabocha	Acorn
Tomatoes	Pumpkin	Spaghetti
Zucchini	Okra	Butternut

Flowers
400° for 15–20 minutes

Broccoli	Cauliflower
Broccolini	Artichokes

Leaves
400° for 15–20 minutes

Cabbages	Kale	Endive
Bok choy	Mustard greens	Romaine
Brussels sprouts	Radicchio	

Seeds and Legumes

400° for 15–20 minutes

Corn	Chinese snow peas
Peas	Green beans
Sugar snap peas	

Roots

425° for 20–40 minutes

May need turning halfway through cooking.

Beets	Celery root	Radishes
Carrots	Parsnip	Rutabaga
	Turnip	

Tubers

450° for 30–45 minutes

May need turning halfway through cooking.

Sweet potatoes	Sunchoke
White potatoes	Jicama

Bulbs

450° for 20–45 minutes

Garlic	Fennel
Onions	Shallots

Stems

400° for 10–15 minutes

Asparagus	Kohlrabi
Celery	Rhubarb
Leek	

Mushrooms/Fungi

425° for 15–20 minutes

HOW
GOOD
FOOD
WORKS
IN THE
KITCHEN

Veggie Fruits and Fruits

GRILLED SUMMER SQUASH
AND
BELL PEPPERS

Serves 4–6

Squash are divided into two categories, summer and winter squash, depending on the season in which they are harvested. One of the main distinguishing characteristics between summer and winter squash is the edible aspect of the skin. Summer squash is harvested in summer before reaching full maturity, which contributes to a shorter shelf life and the skin being edible. Summer squash includes green zucchini, yellow squash and crookneck squash. Summer squash should be harvested when they reach roughly 6–8 inches in size, as the smaller the squash the sweeter the flavor and more tender compared to overgrown zucchini, which tend to be bitter. Once harvested, summer squash can be stored in the refrigerator for up to 10 days. The yellow squash flowers harvested at the end of the zucchini base can also be used in recipes, such as Squash Blossom Pizza with Cauliflower Crust (see recipe page 92) for a beautiful and tasty way to use most of the plant.

Ingredients:

Herb dressing:

½ cup olive oil

¼ cup red wine vinegar

¼ bunch fresh parsley leaves

¼ cup fresh basil leaves

1 tablespoon chopped fresh dill, stems removed

1 tablespoon chopped fresh oregano, stems removed

2 garlic cloves, peeled

½ teaspoon Dijon mustard

1 teaspoon honey

¼ teaspoon kosher salt

¼ teaspoon freshly ground black pepper

Grilled vegetables:

2 zucchini, sliced, ½-inch thick

2 yellow squash, sliced, ½-inch thick

1 red bell pepper, sliced, ½-inch thick

1 orange bell pepper, sliced, ½-inch thick

2 tablespoons olive oil

Method:

1. Herb dressing: In a blender, add the ingredients and blend until smooth. Set aside.

2. Grilled vegetables: Heat the grill to medium-high heat. In a large bowl, place the vegetables and evenly coat with olive oil. Skewer the vegetables and place on the grill for 2–3 minutes on each side until charred and slightly tender. Remove from the heat and drizzle the herb dressing over vegetables. Serve immediately.

Helpful Tips:

If using wooden skewers, make sure to soak them in water before putting them on the grill.

Cut all vegetables to a similar size.

BRAISED SQUASH
AND
MUSHROOMS

Serves 4

Delicata and kabocha are two of the most interesting and flavorful squash. The delicata squash has a striped green and yellow skin, a creamy yellow interior and a flavor similar to that of a butternut squash or sweet potato. Sometimes called the "Japanese pumpkin," the kabocha squash has a sweet potato flavor like the delicata, with a bold green skin and bright orange flesh. Even though these squash are named "winter squash," these varieties are harvested in the fall. The name "winter squash" comes from the squash's ability to be stored throughout the winter season. When choosing a squash, opt for one that is heavy for its size, firm without soft spots or cracks and has a dull finish.

Ingredients:

1 tablespoon canola oil

2–3 pounds delicata or acorn squash, unpeeled, seeded and
  cut into half-moon pieces, ½-inch each

1 tablespoon finely grated fresh ginger

1 garlic clove, minced

4 ounces shiitake mushrooms, stems removed and thinly sliced

½ cup dried apricots, thinly sliced

2 cups vegetable broth

3 tablespoons low sodium soy sauce

1 tablespoon rice vinegar

¼ bunch green onions, thinly sliced

¼ cup chopped peanuts

Method:

1. In a large skillet over medium heat, warm oil until hot and shimmery. Add squash in one layer and let brown, about 2-3 minutes. Turn each squash piece over and brown the other side. Remove squash to a plate and set aside. To the skillet, add ginger, garlic, mushrooms and apricots and sauté until fragrant, about 1–2 minutes.

2. Stir in vegetable broth, soy sauce and vinegar. Bring to a boil. Reduce mixture to a simmer and add squash back to the pan and cover. Cook until squash is tender, about 10–12 minutes. When squash is done, remove to serving bowl and spoon mushroom mixture over the squash.

3. Garnish with green onions and peanuts before serving.

Helpful Tips:

Kabocha squash can be used in this recipe, but its hard skin is difficult to prep.

WINTER SQUASH
WITH
GINGER
AND
PERSIMMONS

Serves 4

The persimmon, a fruit that looks like an odd cousin of the tomato, is the national fruit of Japan and has been cultivated in the US since the 1850s. The most common persimmons in the US are the Fuyu and Hachiya varieties. Fuyu persimmons are enjoyed both under-ripe and ripe, while Hachiya persimmons are best enjoyed when very ripe and soft. Look for persimmons in the grocery store, Asian markets or farmers markets at the peak of their season in October and November. The mild, fruity flavor of the persimmon pairs nicely in this recipe with the nutty and slightly sweet winter squash, which is also in season during the fall.

Ingredients:

Persimmon relish:

2 Fuyu persimmons, diced

1 small orange, zest and juice

½ cup cashews, roasted and chopped

2 tablespoons chiffonaded fresh mint leaves,
   (rolled and sliced thinly)

1 teaspoon minced fresh ginger

¼ teaspoon kosher salt

Squash:

1 tablespoon canola oil

2–3 pounds delicata or acorn squash,
   unpeeled, seeded and thinly cut into ½-inch slices

3 garlic cloves, minced

¼ teaspoon ground cinnamon

⅛ teaspoon ground cardamom

⅛ teaspoon freshly ground black pepper

⅛ teaspoon ground nutmeg

⅛ teaspoon ground cloves

½ cup vegetable broth

Method:

1. Persimmon relish: In a small bowl, combine persimmons, orange juice, zest, cashews, mint, ginger and salt. Set aside in the refrigerator for about 30 minutes before serving.

2. Squash: In a large skillet over medium heat, warm oil until hot and shimmery. Add squash in one layer and let brown, about 2-3 minutes. Turn each squash piece over and brown the other side. Remove squash to a plate and set aside. Add garlic and spices and sauté until fragrant, about 1-2 minutes. Stir in broth to deglaze the pan, lower the heat, add the squash back in and continue cooking until squash are tender, about 8-10 minutes.

3. Top squash with persimmon relish before serving.

Helpful Tips:

If you have a lot of ginger beyond what the recipe calls for, store it, peeled, in a freezer bag. This preserves the ginger and makes it easier to grate on a microplane.

WEEKNIGHT BUTTERNUT SQUASH
AND
PASTA
Serves 4–6

Butternut squash is a staple in the autumn months, but the growing process begins in early summer, as winter squash requires a long growing season of 75–100 days free from frost. Winter squash can be grown in a Native American traditional method called the "three sisters," which is when the squash is grown adjacent to corn and beans for a mutually beneficial growing support system.

Ingredients:

2 quarts water

4 ounces egg noodles or any pasta of your choice

2 tablespoons olive oil

3 tablespoons unsalted butter, sliced into tablespoons

8 ounces cremini mushrooms, sliced ¼-inch thick

2 cups butternut squash, peeled, seeded and diced,
  about ½ medium sized squash

½ teaspoon kosher salt

3 garlic cloves, minced

½ bunch chopped fresh thyme (about 2 tablespoons)

¼ bunch chopped fresh sage (about 2 tablespoons)

¼ bunch chopped fresh parsley (about 2 tablespoons)

½ cup reserved pasta cooking water

Garnish:

chopped fresh parsley

½ cup pine nuts, toasted

Method:

1. Pasta: In a large pot, heat 2 quarts of water to a rolling boil. Add pasta and cook according to package directions. Do not overcook. Reserve ½ cup of pasta water. Drain pasta and transfer to a separate bowl. Cover and set aside.

2. Squash and mushrooms: In a large skillet over medium-high heat, add oil and butter and heat until brown and foamy, about 1-2 minutes. Add mushrooms and sauté about 3-4 minutes. Add squash and salt and continue cooking another 3-4 minutes until squash is tender. Add garlic, thyme, sage and parsley and sauté for 1-2 minutes. Add pasta and pasta water, and gently stir to combine. Continue cooking until sauce coats pasta and vegetables, about 2–3 minutes. Garnish with additional parsley and pine nuts.

Helpful Tips:

Frozen butternut squash can be substituted for fresh.

The skin on a butternut squash is very tough so usually it's peeled before cooking; however, it is edible once it's slow roasted and becomes soft.

The seeds inside can be scooped out, washed and dried, tossed in some oil, salt and pepper and then oven roasted at 350° for 10 minutes.

CRISPY ZUCCHINI WEDGES
WITH
ROMESCO SAUCE

Yields 2 cups

During the summer months, zucchini and squash are plentiful, but how can you tell the difference between zucchini and yellow squash? Because zucchini can be either yellow or green, it may be difficult to differentiate the two based on color alone. Instead, look at the squash's shape. A zucchini is uniformly cylindrical, while a yellow squash is larger towards the bottom and thinner at the neck. When you cut into the two, the yellow squash also contains more seeds. After identifying the difference between the two squash, select the most flavorful zucchini by choosing one that is less than 8 inches in length — these are less watery and bitter than the larger zucchini.

Ingredients:

Romesco sauce:

1 small eggplant, unpeeled and chopped

2 red bell peppers, seeded and chopped

1 red onion, peeled and quartered

4 garlic cloves, peeled

3 tablespoons olive oil, divided use

¼ bunch parsley, stems removed

½ cup unsalted sliced almonds, toasted

2 tablespoons sherry vinegar

½ teaspoon hot paprika

½ teaspoon kosher salt

Crispy zucchini:

oil spray

½ cup finely grated Parmesan cheese

½ cup panko bread crumbs

1 teaspoon dried oregano

1 teaspoon dried thyme

1 teaspoon dried parsley

2 eggs, beaten

2 zucchini, cut into small wedges (about 16 pieces each)

kosher salt

Method:

1. Romesco sauce: Preheat the oven to 450° and line a baking pan with tin foil. Spread eggplant, bell peppers, onion and garlic evenly on the pan and drizzle with 1 tablespoon olive oil. Roast in the oven for 7–8 minutes until the eggplant and peppers are charred and tender. Set aside and let cool for about 10 minutes. Transfer roasted vegetables to a blender and add parsley, almonds, 2 tablespoons olive oil, vinegar, paprika and salt. Blend until smooth. Set aside.

2. Crispy zucchini: Preheat the oven to 450° and line a baking pan with a broiler rack or a cookie cooling rack to provide air circulation so all parts of the zucchini get toasted. Spray the rack with oil. In a medium bowl, combine Parmesan cheese, bread crumbs, oregano, thyme and parsley. Set aside. In a small shallow bowl, whisk the eggs. Working in batches, dip zucchini wedges into the egg then in the breadcrumb mixture and place on the rack. Repeat until all the zucchini wedges are coated with egg and breadcrumbs. Spray oil over zucchini to ensure even browning. Spread evenly, making sure not to overcrowd. Roast on top rack in the oven for 15–20 minutes until crisp on the outside and tender on the inside. Season with salt and serve with Romesco sauce.

Helpful Tips:

A sprinkle of hot paprika on top of the Romesco sauce will give it an additional spicy flavor.

EGGPLANT FRIED RICE
WITH
CHICKEN AND
CASHEWS

Serves 4

Usually, eggplants are purple, but the original eggplant was a vibrant white, hence the "egg" in the name eggplant. Eggplants are ready to be harvested in warmer months, such as July, August and September depending on the climate of the garden and the eggplant variety. The skin should appear glossy and unwrinkled with a uniform color when ready for harvesting. One variety of eggplant called Japanese eggplant is more petite and is harvested when the eggplant is 8–10 inches. Eggplants are great when sautéed, grilled, baked or roasted. Sometimes a sprinkle of salt on top of the sliced eggplant can tenderize it, which contributes to a sweeter taste in cooked dishes. A small amount of salt can help remove excess water and, with that, some of the bitter compounds.

Ingredients:

Brown rice:

½ cup brown rice, washed

1 cup vegetable broth or water

½ teaspoon kosher salt

Sauce:

¼ cup vegetable broth or water

1 tablespoon sesame oil

1 tablespoon low-sodium soy sauce

1 tablespoon brown sugar

1 teaspoon sriracha

Stir fry:

12 ounces boneless chicken thighs,
  skin removed and cut into ½-inch pieces

1 tablespoon cornstarch

1 tablespoon avocado oil

½-inch ginger root, peeled and grated

2 garlic cloves, minced

2–3 Japanese eggplant,
  stems removed and cut diagonally in 1/2-inch slices

1 cup snow peas, strings removed

2 carrots, small diced

½ cup unsalted cashews, toasted

1 egg

¼ bunch green onions, thinly sliced

Method:

1. Brown rice: In a small pot over high heat, add rice, broth or water and salt and bring to a boil. Reduce heat to a simmer and cover. Leave the rice undisturbed for about 35 minutes. Remove from the heat and let sit for an additional 5 minutes. Remove the lid and fluff rice with a fork. Set aside.

2. Sauce: In a small bowl, combine broth or water, sesame oil, soy sauce, brown sugar and sriracha. Set aside.

3. Chicken: In a medium bowl, sprinkle chicken with cornstarch and mix well.

4. Stir fry: In a large sauté pan or wok over medium-high heat, warm oil until hot and shimmery. Add chicken and stir fry until golden, about 6–8 minutes. Add ginger, garlic, eggplant, snow peas, carrots and cashews and stir fry until fragrant, about 1–2 minutes. Stir in sauce and continue cooking until vegetables are tender, about 2–3 minutes. Add rice and cook until rice is heated through, about 1 minute. Create a well in the center of the rice, crack the egg and scramble, mixing it with the ingredients. Remove from the heat and garnish with green onions before serving.

Helpful Tips:

Frozen peas and carrots can be substituted for fresh.

Extra firm tofu dusted in cornstarch can be substituted for chicken thighs.

A cup and a half of day old rice can be substituted and doesn't stick together as much as freshly cooked rice.

ROASTED PEPPERS
AND
SUGAR SNAP PEAS

Serves 4

Mini sweet peppers are sweeter than regular large bell peppers, but they only come in yellow, orange and red–not in traditional green. When selecting mini sweet peppers, look for firm, bright and glossy ones. The same applies to sugar snap peas except they should have a slight bulge to them. If you grab more than you need for this recipe, place the extra peppers and pods in a plastic bag in the refrigerator for up to 2 weeks to use in a stir fry or as an easy grab-and-go snack.

Ingredients:

8 ounces sugar snap peas,
  stems and strings removed from each pod
4–6 mini sweet peppers, stems trimmed and cut lengthwise
1 tablespoon olive oil
1 tablespoon Zesty Ranch Seasoning Blend (see recipe page 253)
kosher salt to taste

Method:

1. Preheat the oven to 450°.

2. In a large bowl, add sugar snap peas and peppers. Combine olive oil and ranch seasoning with vegetables. Mix well. Spread evenly on a baking pan, making sure not to overcrowd.

3. Roast in the oven for 4–5 minutes until snap peas are tender and charred. Remove peas to a bowl and keep warm. Continue roasting the peppers for another 2–3 minutes until crispy and charred. Combine vegetables in the bowl and salt to taste. Serve immediately.

Helpful Tips:

This can also be prepared in a skillet, where the sugar snap peas and peppers are sautéed.

Frozen sugar snap peas work well in this recipe.

PICKLED PEPPERS AND ONIONS

Yields 16 ounces

Pickling vegetables using the hot vinegar method is called fresh pack or quick process pickling. The acetic acid in the vinegar not only gives the vegetables a mouth-watering sour taste, but also prevents the growth of microbes when the pickled vegetables are stored. The most common vinegars used in pickling are distilled white or white wine vinegar. Cider vinegar can be used as well but will result in a darker solution. Vinegar should be between 5% and 7% acidity to properly function as a microbe deterrent.

Ingredients:

2–3 sweet mini peppers, halved, or 1 large red onion, thinly sliced
3–4 sprigs of fresh dill
3 garlic cloves, peeled and cracked
½ cup white vinegar
½ cup water
2 teaspoons canning or pickling salt
½ teaspoon black peppercorns
½ teaspoon mustard seeds
¼ teaspoon red pepper flakes
¼ teaspoon dill seeds

Method:

1. In a sterilized 16-ounce jar, add peppers or onions, dill and garlic.

2. In a medium-sized pot over medium heat, add vinegar, water, salt, peppercorns, mustard seeds, red pepper flakes and dill seeds. Bring to a boil while stirring. Remove from the heat and pour the vinegar mixture over peppers or onions, leaving about a ½-inch of space at the top of the jar.

3. Secure the lid on the jar and allow it to seal by cooling. When cooled, shake well.

4. Store at room temperature out of direct sunlight. If the jar is not sterilized, store it in the refrigerator.

Helpful Tips:

This recipe can be made as "refrigerator vegetables" without heating. Simply add all ingredients to the jar, shake well and store in the refrigerator for up to a week.

CUCUMBER
AND
MELON
GAZPACHO

Serves 6

It's important to harvest cucumbers as soon as they are ready, or else they will become bitter. Depending on the cucumber variety, the size at harvest time will also differ. Pickling cucumbers will be harvested at 2 inches long, dill pickles at 4–6 inches long, slicing cucumbers at 6–8 inches long and burpless cucumbers at 10 inches long. In warm soil, most cucumbers will be ready for harvest in 6 weeks. Refrigerate immediately after picking, and store loosely in a plastic bag for up to 3 days.

Ingredients:

1 small cantaloupe, rind removed, seeded and chopped
1 cucumber, peeled and seeds removed
1 cup cherry tomatoes, halved
¼ cup red wine vinegar
¼ teaspoon Garam Masala Blend (see recipe page 253)
½ bunch fresh mint, stems removed
¼ teaspoon kosher salt
¼ cup olive oil

Garnish:
¼ cup Pickled Red Onions (see recipe page 204)
¼ cup crumbled feta cheese
cucumbers, tomatoes, mint and almonds

Method:

1. Set aside a small portion of sliced cucumbers, tomatoes and mint for garnish.

2. In a blender or food processor, add cantaloupe, cucumber, cherry tomatoes, red wine vinegar, Garam Masala Blend, mint and salt. Pulse until the desired consistency is reached. With the motor running, drizzle in the oil. Transfer to an airtight container and chill for at least 1 hour.

3. Transfer to a serving bowl and garnish with Pickled Red Onions, feta cheese, cucumber slices, tomato halves, mint and almonds.

Helpful Tips:

When pulsing for the desired consistency, puree longer for a smoother gazpacho, and pulse just a few times for a chunky gazpacho.

Garam Masala Blend is utilized in South Asian cooking and has a unique sweet and fragrant flavor.

Cucumber and Melon Salad with Roasted Whole Fish

CUCUMBER
AND
MELON
SALAD
WITH
ROASTED
WHOLE FISH

Serves 4

Cucumbers and melons are distant cousins of the same plant family, *Cucumis sativus*. Although cucumbers are thought to be a vegetable, they are actually a fruit because they contain seeds and ovaries. Cucumbers are separated into two varieties, bush cucumbers or vining cucumbers, and the difference can best suit your garden based on the size and style of your beds or trellises. Vining cucumbers are known for their long and winding vines that grow up to 6 feet long in garden beds and feature curly tendrils that climb up the cages commonly used to provide structure for the growing plant. Bush cucumbers grow on very short vines, only 1 to 2 feet long.

Honeydews, like cucumbers, are also a warm-season crop that requires lots of space in the garden due to their far-reaching vines that grow outward. When the flesh of a honeydew turns pale green, it's ready to be harvested — which will be about 100 days from the first sprout.

Ingredients:

Yogurt dressing:

1 cup plain Greek yogurt, strained

1 lemon, juiced

6 cloves garlic, roasted and smashed into a paste

1 tablespoon finely chopped mint leaves

1 tablespoon finely chopped dill, stems removed

½ teaspoon salt

½ teaspoon freshly ground black pepper

2 tablespoons extra virgin olive oil

½ English cucumber, peeled and grated
   (squeeze out excess moisture with a paper towel)

Fish:

4 1–1½ pounds fish (branzino, trout, etc.),
   cleaned, scaled and skin scored on the bias

8 tablespoons olive oil

2 teaspoons kosher salt

1 teaspoon freshly ground black pepper

4 tablespoons unsalted butter

4 garlic cloves, minced

1 bunch fresh mint leaves

1 bunch fresh dill

4 lemons, sliced ¼-inch thick

Salad:

4 small cucumbers, thinly sliced lengthwise

½ honeydew melon, rind removed, seeded and thinly sliced

2 cups dandelion greens

½ cup spiced walnuts (see Sweet and Spicy Nuts recipe page 260), chopped

¼ cup chopped fresh dill

1 lemon, juiced

Method:

1. Dressing: In a small bowl, whisk together dressing ingredients until smooth. Set aside in the refrigerator.

2. Fish: Preheat the oven to 450°. In a large roasting pan, place and evenly drizzle 2 tablespoons of olive oil on both sides and inside the cavity of each fish. Season each with ½ teaspoon salt and ¼ teaspoon of freshly ground black pepper. Stuff each cavity with one quarter of the butter, garlic, mint, dill and lemon slices. Roast for 15–20 minutes or until an internal thermometer reads 135˚.

3. Salad: To serve, place cucumbers, melon slices and dandelion greens on a platter with the fish. Top with walnuts, fresh dill and a dollop of yogurt dressing and lemon juice. Garnish with dill sprigs.

Helpful Tips:

Use a vegetable peeler or a mandoline to make very thin ribbon slices of melon and cucumber.

If you can't find dandelion greens, substitute arugula or watercress.

GRILLED WATERMELON, SHRIMP
AND
HERB SALAD

Serves 4

Watermelons grow during the warm months and are planted in rows, often in raised beds, and are ready for harvesting just three months after planting. The watermelon should be free of any cuts or bruises. Most of a watermelon's weight is water, so it should feel heavy for its size. How do you know when a watermelon is ripe? Ripe watermelons have a pale yellow spot on the underside which indicates where it was sitting on the ground and ripened in the field. Also, if you knock on the watermelon, it should have a deep hollow sound.

Ingredients:

Watermelon and shrimp:

3 tablespoons olive oil

3 garlic cloves, minced

1 tablespoon smoked paprika

1 teaspoon dried oregano

½ teaspoon kosher salt

1 small watermelon, cut into 1-inch thick wedges

12 ounces jumbo shrimp, peeled and deveined, tails on

Salad:

2 cups arugula

1 bunch fresh lemon basil, stems removed

1 bunch fresh mint, stems removed

½ cup pistachios, toasted and chopped

½ red onion, thinly sliced

2 tablespoons shaved Parmesan cheese

2 tablespoons olive oil

1 lemon, juiced

Method:

1. Grilled watermelon and shrimp: In a medium bowl, combine olive oil, garlic, smoked paprika, oregano and salt. Heat the grill to medium-high heat. Place the cut watermelon on a baking pan lined with parchment paper. On a skewer, thread 3–4 pieces of shrimp and repeat until all shrimp are on the skewers. Place on the baking pan and brush the olive oil mixture evenly over both sides of shrimp skewers and watermelon. Grill the watermelon and shrimp skewers, about 2–3 minutes on each side, until charred with grill marks and shrimp are lightly browned and opaque. Remove from the heat and let them cool.

2. Salad: On a large serving platter, place arugula, basil and mint. Then top them with grilled watermelon and shrimp skewers. Garnish with pistachios, red onions and Parmesan cheese. Drizzle salad with olive oil and lemon juice.

Helpful Tips:

If you are using wooden skewers, make sure to soak them in water first.

To remove watermelon rind: Cut the top and bottom off the watermelon. Place the watermelon on one cut side and slice away the rind on each side. Turn the melon on its side and cut it into sections roughly 1 inch thick.

PUMPKIN PIE PARFAIT

Serves 6

The pumpkin variety is very important when growing your own pumpkins or purchasing from your local grocery store, as not all pumpkins are ideal for roasting. The smaller varieties, such as "small sugar pumpkins" or "New England pie pumpkins," are some of the common roasting ones. The bigger pumpkins are less sweet and best saved for carving fun designs. Pumpkins are planted around July in the southern states and take about three months to fully mature depending on the variety. Pumpkins will be ready to harvest when the outside flesh is a deep dark orange and when a hollow sound is heard when the rind is tapped. Don't throw the seeds away as they can be cleaned and roasted for a snack or a salad topping.

Ingredients:

Pumpkin puree:

2 cups plain Greek yogurt, strained
1 cup pumpkin puree
2 tablespoons maple syrup
1 tablespoon pumpkin pie spice

Gingersnap topping:

1 cup unsalted walnuts, toasted
½ cup gingersnap cookies (about 10–15)
¼ cup brown sugar

Whipped cream:

1 cup heavy whipping cream
¼ cup powdered sugar
1 teaspoon vanilla extract

Candied pumpkin cubes:

candied pumpkin cubes
pumpkin spice

Method:

1. Pumpkin puree: In a large bowl using a hand mixer, blend together the yogurt, pumpkin puree, maple syrup and pumpkin pie spice until smooth. Set aside in the refrigerator.

2. Gingersnap topping: In a food processor, combine walnuts, gingersnaps and brown sugar and pulse until crumbly. Set aside until ready to use.

3. Whipped cream: In a mixing bowl, combine cream, sugar and vanilla extract. Beat on high speed until the mixture develops soft peaks.

4. Parfait: Layer each parfait glass ⅓ full with the puree, top with gingersnap topping and then whipped cream and complete with puree, gingersnap topping, whipped cream, candied pumpkin cubes and a sprinkle of pumpkin spice.

Helpful Tips:

Candied pumpkin can usually be found in the international aisle or in the bulk grocery section.

Fresh pumpkin can be used by roasting one 2–3 pound sugar pumpkin that has been halved and seeds removed. Brush with oil and place cut-side down on a baking pan lined with parchment paper. Bake at 350°for 45 minutes or until fork tender. Scoop out the cooked flesh and use as a substitute for canned pumpkin.

Overnight Oats

BLUEBERRY OVERNIGHT OATS

Serves 4

Blueberries are a sweet summer treat. With proper maintenance and care, blueberry bushes can be a beautiful and edible addition to your home garden. Blueberries grow on bushes in a range of sizes, with most plants producing a harvest of berries in their third year. To properly prune a blueberry bush, begin by removing all flowers as they bloom in the first two years — this promotes greater growth of the plant and encourages a larger harvest in the years to come. Starting in the plant's fourth year, prune dead, weak or old branches in the beginning of spring while the bush is still dormant. The goal of pruning is to open up the bush so light can reach all branches. Branches become less productive as they age, so make sure to cut back any that are roughly 6 years or older, or about 1 inch in diameter. When harvesting blueberries, leave them on the bush for a few days after they turn blue. This ensures that the berries you collect are deliciously ripe and sweet.

Ingredients:

Oat base:

2 cups whole rolled oats

1½ cups milk (dairy or dairy alternative)

1 cup plain Greek yogurt (or silken tofu)

2 tablespoons chia seeds

1 tablespoon honey or another liquid sweetener

1 teaspoon vanilla extract

½ tablespoon ground flax seeds

Blueberry maple (1 serving):

½ cup blueberries

2 tablespoons chopped pecans

1 tablespoon maple syrup

Method:

1. Overnight oat base: In a large bowl, combine oats, milk, yogurt or tofu, chia seeds, honey or liquid sweetener, vanilla extract and flax seeds. Portion equal amounts into four containers.

2. Topping: Add choice of topping to each mixture. Cover and refrigerate overnight.

Helpful Tips:

Portion the oats into mason jars for an on-the-go morning breakfast.

Additional Topping Variations:

Apple, pear and walnut (1 serving):

¼ cup diced pear

¼ cup diced apple

2 tablespoons chopped walnuts

⅛ teaspoon ground cinnamon

Banana, almond and chocolate (1 serving):

1 banana, cut into slices

2 tablespoons chopped almonds

2 teaspoons semi-sweet chocolate chips

2 teaspoons unsweetened coconut chips

Nut butter and preserves (1 serving):

½ cup diced strawberries

2 tablespoons chopped peanuts

1 tablespoon peanut butter

2 teaspoons strawberry preserves

SALTED CHOCOLATE DATES

Yields 20 dates

Growing from a date palm, or "tree of life," Medjool dates are dark, amber brown with a slightly wrinkled skin and a soft, creamy flesh. Dates are primarily grown in the Middle East or in other areas with high heat and low humidity, like southwest Arizona. The small brown jewel is often referred to as nature's candy, and this recipe uses the date's natural sweetness to create a delectable treat. The high sugar content of Medjool dates is complemented and subdued by dark chocolate, walnuts and salt.

Ingredients:

20 Medjool dates

1 cup unsalted walnut halves, roasted

8 ounces dark chocolate chips, more than 65% cocoa

1 teaspoon ground cinnamon

1 teaspoon ground turmeric

1 tablespoon coconut oil

1 teaspoon large flake salt (Maldon salt recommended)

Method:

1. Line a baking pan with wax or parchment paper.

2. Slice the dates in the middle but not all the way through and remove the pits. Place 1–2 walnut halves inside each date and securely close with a toothpick. Set aside.

3. In a double boiler over low heat, combine chocolate, cinnamon, turmeric and coconut oil, stirring until the mixture is melted and smooth.

4. Using a toothpick, dip each date into the chocolate mixture. Place chocolate-dipped dates on the pan and sprinkle with salt. Remove toothpicks and place in the refrigerator for about 30 minutes or until the chocolate is set.

Helpful Tips:

Store in an airtight container in the refrigerator for up to 1 week.

Substitute just about any nut for walnuts.

Add orange zest to the chocolate mixture in a double boiler for a citrus flavor.

HOW
GOOD
FOOD
WORKS
IN THE
KITCHEN

Flower Buds and Flowers

GRILLED CAULIFLOWER STEAKS
WITH
BEEF TENDERLOINS
AND
HERB AIOLI

Serves 4

Cauliflower can be found in several colors — white, green, purple and orange. Although each may look different, the taste is still the same. The colors are natural and come from antioxidants, similar to the way cabbage comes in green and red.

Ingredients:

Herb aioli:

3 tablespoons light mayonnaise

1 tablespoon olive oil

1 tablespoon sherry vinegar

1 garlic clove, peeled

2 tablespoons chopped fresh parsley, stems removed

1 tablespoon chopped fresh thyme, stems removed

1 teaspoon chopped fresh rosemary, stems removed

**Cauliflower steaks and
  beef tenderloin fillets:**

1 cauliflower head, core trimmed,
  leaves retained, and cut into 4 "steaks"

4 beef tenderloin fillets (about 12 ounces)

1 red onion, cut in wedges

3 tablespoons olive oil

1 tablespoon Grilling Seasoning Blend
  (see recipe page 254)

kosher salt and freshly ground black pepper to taste

Assembly:

2 cups arugula

1 lemon, cut into wedges

1 tablespoon olive oil for drizzling

Maldon sea salt flakes to taste

Method:

1. Herb aioli: In a blender or food processor, mix mayonnaise, olive oil, sherry vinegar, garlic, parsley, thyme and rosemary. Blend until smooth. Cover and set aside in the refrigerator.

2. Cauliflower steaks and beef tenderloin fillets: Heat the grill to medium-high heat. On a baking pan lined with parchment paper, place cauliflower steaks, tenderloin fillets and onions. Drizzle both sides with olive oil and season liberally with Grilling Seasoning Blend. Salt and pepper to taste. Place onions, cauliflower steaks and fillets on the grill for about 5–7 minutes each side, until the tenderloins reach the desired doneness, between 130° and 140°, and vegetables are tender and slightly charred.

3. Serving: Place onions, cauliflower steaks and tenderloin fillets on a bed of arugula and top with herb aioli, a squeeze of lemon, a drizzle of olive oil and some Maldon sea salt flakes.

Helpful Tips:

Substitute pork chops or pork tenderloin for beef tenderloin fillets. Adjust cooking time if needed.

CAULIFLOWER HASH BROWNS

Serves 4

Cauliflower is thought to have first been domesticated in the Mediterranean region in the Middle Ages. It was not until the 17th century that cauliflower made its way to France and England. Toward the beginning of the 20th century, due to large European migration, cauliflower gained popularity. There are hundreds of varieties around the world. The most popular that grows in North America is called the Northern European annuals since it was developed in Germany in the 18th century.

Ingredients:

1 large cauliflower head
1 large egg
2 egg whites or 4 tablespoons liquid egg whites
½ cup finely chopped green onion
¼ onion, grated (about 2 tablespoons)
1 cup shredded cheddar cheese
3 tablespoons cornstarch
kosher salt to taste
freshly ground black pepper
2 tablespoons olive oil

Method:

1. Use a box grater to grate entire cauliflower head. Transfer to a medium bowl and add egg, egg whites, onions, cheddar and cornstarch. Season with salt and pepper.

2. In a large cast iron pan or griddle over medium-high heat, warm the oil until hot and shimmery.

3. Using a 3 ounce scoop, add cauliflower mixture to the pan, shaping it into hash brown pancakes. Let them cook for 3–5 minutes until brown and crispy, then flip over and cook for another 3–5 minutes.

4. Let the cauliflower hash browns rest on a plate for a few minutes before serving.

Helpful Tips:

If the cauliflower mixture produces too much liquid, add a tablespoon or two of dried potato flakes to help bind it together.

"TAKE-OUT" SWEET CHILI CAULIFLOWER

Serves 4–6

Growing cauliflower can be tricky with such problems as poorly developed heads or hollowed stems. But it's worth trying since cauliflower can be used in so many recipes. The cauliflower plant grows best in moderate temperatures of 70–85° with plenty of sun and moist soil. Long periods of sun in hot summer weather can cause the cauliflower heads to develop a red-purple hue. It can take as long as three months from seed to harvest.

Ingredients:

2 tablespoons canola oil
1 tablespoon sesame oil
2 garlic cloves, minced
2 tablespoons honey
2 tablespoons plus 2 teaspoons ground chili paste (recommended sambal oelek chili paste)
¼ teaspoon kosher salt
1 cauliflower head (about 1 pound), cut into equal-sized florets

Garnish:
1 Thai chili pepper, thinly sliced
¼ bunch green onions, thinly sliced or cut into 3-inch pieces
sesame seeds
red chili flakes to taste

Method:

1. Preheat oven to 400°.

2. In a small bowl, combine canola oil, sesame oil, garlic, honey, chili paste and salt. Mix well. Pour over the cauliflower florets.

3. Spread cauliflower evenly and mix well on a baking pan lined with parchment paper, making sure not to overcrowd.

4. Roast in the oven for 20–25 minutes until crisp on the outside and tender on the inside. Remove and place in a large bowl, add the oil mixture and gently fold until evenly coated.

5. Garnish with Thai chili slices, green onions, sesame seeds and red chili flakes to taste before serving.

Helpful Tips:

Remember to toss or turn the cauliflower midway through roasting.

Thai chili peppers are considered some of the hottest, so a small slice can give off a lot of heat.

CAULIFLOWER, PARMESAN LENTILS, TOMATO COMPOTE
AND
CRISPY SNAPPER

Serves 4

The edible portion of the cauliflower is the large central head, called the curd. Harvest is ready when the curds are still compact but large enough to eat, about 6–8 inches in diameter. Most cauliflower is sold in the grocery store tightly wrapped in cellophane, but it's best to remove the wrap because it can trap moisture and promote rot. We recommend keeping the cauliflower in a plastic bag lined with paper towels to absorb excess moisture and storing it in the crisper drawer in the refrigerator for 7–14 days.

Ingredients:

Tomato compote:

2 tablespoons olive oil

2 shallots, thinly sliced

1 tablespoon chopped fresh thyme, stems removed

4 medium-size heirloom tomatoes, chopped
   about 4 cups)

¼ teaspoon kosher salt

½ teaspoon granulated sugar

Parmesan lentils:

½ cup lentils

1 cup vegetable broth

1 tablespoon olive oil

½ teaspoon garlic powder

2 tablespoons finely shredded Parmesan cheese

⅛ teaspoon kosher salt

Herb cauliflower:

2 tablespoons olive oil

½ pound cauliflower head (about ½ a large head),
   cut into bite-sized florets

2 garlic cloves, minced

½ teaspoon dried oregano

½ teaspoon dried rosemary

½ teaspoon dried thyme

⅛ teaspoon kosher salt

½ lemon, juiced

Crispy snapper:

4 red snapper fillets, skin-on (about 1 pound)

⅛ teaspoon kosher salt

⅛ teaspoon freshly ground black pepper

3 tablespoons canola oil

1 lemon, halved, roasted

Helpful Tips:

It's best to make the tomato compote ahead of time. When you are ready to start preparing this dish, organize all the ingredients so each part is ready at the same time.

Method:

1. Tomato compote: In a small heavy bottom pot over medium heat, warm the olive oil until hot and shimmery. Add shallots and thyme and sauté until lightly browned, about 1-2 minutes. Reduce heat to low and add tomatoes, salt and sugar. Continue cooking uncovered for 40-50 minutes or until thickened, making sure to stir often. Set aside.

2. Parmesan lentils: Preheat the oven to 400° and line a baking pan with parchment paper. In a small heavy-bottomed pot, combine lentils and vegetable broth. Bring to a boil over high heat. Reduce heat to low, cover and continue cooking for 15 minutes. Drain lentils and pat dry. In a small bowl, mix olive oil, cooked lentils and garlic powder. Spread evenly on the pan, making sure not to overcrowd. Roast in the oven for 20–25 minutes until the lentils are crispy but not burnt and lemon halves are brown. Sprinkle Parmesan cheese and salt evenly over the lentils and return to the oven for an additional 3–5 minutes or until the Parmesan is crispy. Set aside.

3. Herb cauliflower: In a large cast iron pan over medium heat, warm oil until hot and shimmery. Add cauliflower and allow to brown before stirring, about 2–3 minutes. Stir cauliflower, then add garlic, oregano, rosemary and thyme and continue cooking until garlic is fragrant, about 1–2 minutes. Stir in salt and lemon juice. Remove from the heat and keep warm.

4. Snapper: Pat the fillets dry and season with salt and pepper, skin-side up. Heat oil in a large cast iron pan over medium-high heat until hot and shimmery. Add two fillets skin-side down and allow skin to crisp and unstick before flipping, about 2–3 minutes. Turn fillets and finish cooking another 2–3 minutes or until internal temperature reaches 135°. Set aside. Keep warm. Repeat the process for the other two fillets.

5. To assemble: Serve snapper fillets on top of herb cauliflower and Parmesan lentils with tomato compote on the side, garnish with roasted lemon halves.

SQUASH BLOSSOM PIZZA
WITH
CAULIFLOWER CRUST

Serves 4

Squash blossoms are deliciously edible. When clipping the blossoms from the plant, make sure to leave the ones closest to the stalk and look for a small bulb under the flower since these are where the female blossoms will turn into beautiful yellow squash. Make sure you pick them first thing in the morning when the flowers are in bloom, and then store them in the refrigerator until they are ready to use. They can be eaten raw, sautéed or stuffed and baked. If purchased from the store, make sure to use the blossoms as quickly as possible.

The crust is made with cooked cauliflower. Because cauliflower is 92% water, it's necessary to drain and squeeze it before using it in dishes like this. But once dried out, it resembles the texture of a flour crust.

Ingredients:

Crust:

1 cauliflower head, cut into florets
   (medium to large head)
½ cup grated Parmesan cheese
1 cup shredded mozzarella cheese
1 teaspoon Italian Seasoning Blend
   (see recipe page 253)
¼ teaspoon kosher salt
2 large eggs

Pizza:

½ cup Carrot Top Pesto (see recipe page 256)
1 small zucchini, sliced into strips with a vegetable peeler
1 small yellow squash,
   thinly sliced with a vegetable peeler
12–15 squash blossoms, stems trimmed
¼ cup ricotta cheese
2 tablespoons grated Parmesan cheese
¼ cup shredded mozzarella cheese
freshly ground black pepper to taste

Method:

1. Crust: Preheat the oven to 425° and line a rimmed baking pan with parchment paper. Place cauliflower in a food processor and pulse until it resembles rice. Place riced cauliflower in a microwave-safe bowl. Cover loosely with a lid or a damp towel. Cook on high in the microwave for 4–6 minutes or until the cauliflower is tender. Allow to cool. Transfer to a clean towel and squeeze to drain out as much water as possible. Then, add to a food processor squeezed cauliflower, Parmesan cheese, mozzarella cheese, Italian Seasoning Blend, salt and eggs. Pulse until the ingredients are well blended and a dough forms. Transfer cauliflower dough to the baking pan and form into a round pizza shape. Bake in the oven until golden brown, about 15–20 minutes. Remove from the oven.

2. Pizza: While the crust is baking, prepare the Carrot Top Pesto. Spread the pesto across the crust and top with zucchini slices, squash slices and squash blossoms. Dollop small portions of ricotta cheese and lightly sprinkle Parmesan and mozzarella cheese on top. Season with pepper. Transfer the pizza to the oven and bake until squash blossoms are golden and cheese is melted and bubbly.

Helpful Tips:

If cauliflower mixture produces too much liquid, add a tablespoon or two of dried potato flakes to help bind it together.

Frozen cauliflower rice is also available in the frozen section and works well in pizza crusts. Make sure you press out as much water as possible.

LEMON BROCCOLINI
WITH
MANCHEGO, PINE NUTS
AND
OLIVES

Serves 4

Broccolini is a cross-breed of broccoli and Chinese broccoli. The florets are on the end, but the stems are long and thin. It is milder in flavor and more tender than broccoli. It usually costs a little more since a bunch of broccoli usually consists of 2–3 stalks, while a bunch of broccolini has 15 to 20 stalks. It's much more time-consuming to cut at harvest.

Ingredients:

2 tablespoons olive oil

1 tablespoon lemon juice and zest of 1 lemon

2 garlic cloves, minced

¼ teaspoon kosher salt

¼ teaspoon freshly ground black pepper

½ teaspoon hot Spanish paprika

1 pound broccolini, stems trimmed

2 lemons, halved

2 tablespoons pine nuts, toasted

¼ cup green olives, thinly sliced lengthwise

2 tablespoons finely grated Manchego cheese

Method:

1. Preheat the oven to 425°.

2. In a large bowl, combine olive oil, 1 tablespoon lemon juice, garlic, salt, pepper and paprika. Add broccolini and mix. Spread evenly on a baking sheet, and add 4 lemon halves, cut side down. Roast for 12–15 minutes.

3. Sprinkle with toasted pine nuts, olive slices, zest and Manchego cheese, and squeeze lemon halves over broccolini.

Helpful Tips:

Manchego cheese is made in Spain from the milk of Manchega sheep. If unavailable, substitute Italian pecorino, which is also made from sheep's milk.

BROCCOLI
WITH
QUINOA
AND
CRISPY CHICKPEAS

Serves 4

Broccoli is grown for its edible flower buds. It should be harvested when the head has become large but still has tight flower buds. It's past its prime when the buds begin to enlarge and open to yellow flowers. When grown from a seed, it takes 70 to 100 days to harvest. Cut the broccoli head with 5 to 6 inches of the stem, leaving the base of the plant intact. After the first harvest, it will continue to produce one or two more smaller heads on the stem over the next few week's.

Ingredients:

Dijon dressing:

3 tablespoons olive oil

2 tablespoons apple cider vinegar

1 tablespoon Dijon mustard

2 teaspoons honey

1 garlic clove, minced

½ teaspoon smoked paprika

Chickpeas:

1 can chickpeas or garbanzo beans (15 ounces),
  drained, rinsed and patted dry

1 tablespoon olive oil

kosher salt to taste

freshly ground black pepper to taste

Broccoli:

1 pound broccoli (1 medium head),
  cut into equal-sized florets

1 tablespoon olive oil

kosher salt and freshly ground black pepper to taste

Quinoa:

½ cup quinoa, uncooked, rinsed and drained

¾ cup vegetable broth

½ teaspoon kosher salt

Garnish:

¼ cup slivered almonds, unsalted and toasted

1 sweet apple, thinly sliced

Method:

1. Dijon dressing: In a 12-ounce mason jar or similar container, combine olive oil, vinegar, mustard, honey, garlic and paprika. Secure the lid, shake the container until the contents are mixed well. Set aside.

2. Chickpeas: Preheat the oven to 400°. In a small bowl, mix chickpeas, olive oil, salt and pepper. Place them on a baking pan lined with parchment paper and bake for 40–45 minutes until they are crispy. Make sure to shake the pan every 10 minutes or so until done.

3. Broccoli: In a bowl, mix broccoli, olive oil, salt and pepper. Spread them evenly on a baking pan lined with parchment paper, making sure not to overcrowd. Roast in the 400° oven for 20–25 minutes until broccoli is crisp on the outside and tender on the inside.

4. Quinoa: In a small pot over high heat, add quinoa, broth and salt. Bring to a boil. Reduce the heat to low, cover and continue cooking for 12 minutes. Turn the heat off and let stand for an additional 5 minutes. Do not disturb. Uncover and fluff quinoa with a fork.

5. Assembly: In a large bowl, combine quinoa, broccoli, chickpeas, Dijon dressing, almonds and apple slices.

Helpful Tips:

If you have extra crispy chickpeas, they can be stored in an airtight container. They make an excellent afternoon snack.

WEEKNIGHT GARLIC
AND
HERB BUTTER BROCCOLI

Serves 4

If you are growing broccoli, it's best to harvest during the cool morning hours and refrigerate as soon as possible. Unwashed broccoli heads can be stored in the refrigerator for three to five days. Blanched broccoli freezes well and maintains its quality for up to three months. The leaves and stems of broccoli plants are edible too. Use them as you would kale or collards.

Ingredients:

1 broccoli head (about 1 pound), florets only,
   cut into equal-sized pieces
2 tablespoons unsalted butter
1 tablespoon water
2 teaspoons salt-free Italian seasoning
1 teaspoon garlic powder
½ teaspoon kosher salt
¼ teaspoon freshly ground black pepper
⅓ cup shredded Parmesan cheese

Method:

1. Place broccoli, butter and water and in a microwave-safe bowl and sprinkle with seasonings.

2. Cover loosely with a lid or a damp paper towel.

3. Cook on high in the microwave for 3 minutes and check broccoli for desired doneness. Continue cooking in 1 minute intervals until broccoli reaches desired texture.

4. Stir well before serving to evenly coat broccoli. Toss with Parmesan cheese.

Helpful Tips:

Substitute a bag of cut broccoli to skip a few steps.

SHAVED ARTICHOKE AND ROASTED BEET SALAD

Serves 4

Artichokes may appear a bit daunting. The outside petals are hard and spiky, making them appear almost inedible. The only parts you can't eat are the hairy choke inside and the sharp, fibrous outer portion of the leaves. The choke isn't poisonous, nor is the tough part of the leaves, but they're not recommended to eat. However, once you peel away the outer shell and choke, inside is a beautiful artichoke heart that is tender when cooked and resembles a meaty texture.

Ingredients:

Beets and artichokes:

2 baby golden beets, washed and peeled,
   cut into quarters
8 globe artichokes
2 tablespoons olive oil
kosher salt and freshly ground black pepper to taste

Lemon basil vinaigrette:

½ cup extra virgin olive oil
¼ cup champagne vinegar
1 cup lemon basil (can substitute American basil)
1 shallot, minced
1 garlic clove, minced
2 tablespoons grated Parmesan cheese
2 teaspoons honey
pinch of kosher salt

Salad assembly:

¼ red onion, thinly sliced
1 cup watercress
½ cup candied walnuts
   (see Candied Nuts recipe on page 260)
¼ cup crumbled goat cheese

Method:

1. Beets: Preheat oven to 400°. On a baking sheet lined with parchment paper, roast the beets for 20–25 minutes until tender on the inside. Remove and set aside.

2. Artichokes: Prep artichokes by trimming the stem and top, and remove the outer layer of the leaves. Cut the artichoke in half lengthwise and remove the fuzzy center with a spoon. Heat the grill to medium-high heat. Drizzle olive oil evenly over both sides of artichokes and season liberally with salt and pepper. Grill the artichokes for 2–3 minutes on each side until charred and slightly tender. Remove from the heat and let cool.

3. Lemon basil vinaigrette: In a blender or food processor, add the ingredients and blend them until smooth. Store in an airtight container in the refrigerator for up to 2 days.

4. Salad assembly: Thinly slice the artichokes and red onion lengthwise. In a large bowl, combine the artichokes, beets, red onions, watercress, walnuts and goat cheese. Drizzle the lemon basil vinaigrette over the salad.

Helpful Tips:

Wear a pair of gloves when working with beets, as the color can stain your hands.

ARTICHOKES
WITH
FARRO RISOTTO
AND
WHIPPED FETA

Serves 4

The majority of commercial artichoke production in the United States is along coastal sections of central California where the weather is perfect for growth. In South Texas, producers are successfully harvesting artichokes as annuals where the seedlings are raised in greenhouses and transplanted to the fields during the late summer and fall. In the spring, they are ready for harvest. In general, artichokes are a low maintenance vegetable crop since they don't require much besides sun and water. The artichoke flower buds are the edible portion, but only before the flowers come into bloom. Once the buds bloom, the structure changes and they're not edible.

Ingredients:

3 cups vegetable broth

2 tablespoons olive oil

1 shallot, finely minced

2 garlic cloves, minced

¼ bunch rainbow chard, leaves roughly chopped and stems small diced, set aside separately

1 bag frozen artichokes (10 ounces), thawed and diced

2 tablespoons chopped fresh thyme

1 cup farro, rinsed

½ teaspoon kosher salt

pinch of freshly ground black pepper

¼ cup white wine

¼ cup crumbled feta

1 cup white beans, rinsed and drained

¼ cup unsalted walnuts, chopped and toasted

Method:

1. In a medium saucepan, bring the vegetable broth to a simmer and keep warm.

2. In a large cast iron pan over medium heat, warm the oil until hot and shimmery. Add shallots, garlic, chard stems, artichokes and thyme, and sauté until the garlic is fragrant, about 1–2 minutes. Add farro and cook, stirring frequently until farro is coated with oil and slightly toasted, about 2–3 minutes. Add salt, pepper and wine, and stir frequently until evaporated, about 1–2 minutes.

3. Reduce the heat to medium-low and add ½ cup of warm broth, stirring frequently until absorbed, about 3–4 minutes. Continue adding the remaining broth, ½ cup at a time, until absorbed and the farro mixture is creamy and cooked through, about 20–25 minutes.

4. Stir in feta, white beans and chard leaves, and continue cooking until feta has melted and chard leaves are wilted, about 2–3 minutes. Top with toasted walnuts.

Helpful Tips:

Hot broth or stock serves as a melding agent, releasing the farro's starch and making it creamy. The broth must be simmering because its heat ensures even, continuous and thorough cooking. Make sure to use aromatic, unsalted broth that's not too concentrated—if it's too flavorful, it will overpower the farro.

For the oven method: Farro risotto can also be prepared in a preheated 350° oven. You'll need to use a Dutch oven instead of a pan and follow the steps above until the broth is added. At that point, add all the broth to the sauté mixture. Combine everything and bring to a boil. Cover and place in the oven for 30 minutes until the farro is just slightly underdone. Some liquid will remain, and it will be slightly chewy. Remove from the oven and place on the stove top on medium-high heat. Add feta, beans and chard leaves. Top with toasted walnuts and serve immediately.

BLISTERED SHISHITO PEPPERS
WITH
BONITO
AND
EDAMAME

Serves 4

Shishito peppers are generally mild and slightly sweet, but watch out: One out of every 10 Shishito peppers can make your eyes water. These blistered peppers are irresistible, making it hard to eat just one. The typical heat range runs from 100 to 1,000 heat units on the Scoville scale, which isn't very hot. A typical jalapeno pepper is a lot hotter and can range from 2,500 to 8,000 on the scale.

Ingredients:

Crispy edamame:
1 tablespoon sesame oil
½ cup unsalted edamame, shelled
½ teaspoon garlic powder

Sauce:
¼-inch piece fresh ginger root,
   peeled and grated
1 garlic clove, minced
2 teaspoons soy sauce
2 tablespoons light mayonnaise

Shishito peppers:
1 tablespoon canola oil
½ pound shishito peppers (about 20 peppers)
¼-inch piece fresh ginger root, peeled and grated
1 garlic clove, minced
2 tablespoons soy sauce
2 broccoli stems, shaved
1 teaspoon toasted sesame seeds
1 teaspoon Bonito flakes
   (found in the international section of the grocery store)

Method:

1. Crispy edamame: Preheat the oven to 400° and line a baking pan with parchment paper. In a small bowl, mix sesame oil and edamame. Spread edamame evenly on the pan, making sure not to overcrowd. Roast in the oven for 15–20 minutes until the edamame is crispy but not burnt. Sprinkle garlic powder evenly over edamame, and return to the oven for an additional 2–3 minutes. Remove and stir well. Set aside.

2. Sauce: In a small bowl, combine ginger, garlic, soy sauce and mayonnaise. Set aside.

3. Shishito peppers: Heat canola oil in a large cast iron pan over medium-high heat until hot and shimmery. Add shishito peppers and stir occasionally, allowing the peppers to blister on all sides, about 3–4 minutes. Add ginger, garlic and soy sauce, and sauté for 1 minute to release the flavors. Remove from the heat.

4. Assemble a large platter with blistered peppers over a bed of shaved broccoli stem and crispy edamame and sprinkle with sesame seeds and Bonito flakes. Serve with the sauce on the side.

Helpful Tips:

Bonito flakes come from fish that has been boiled, smoked, dried completely and shaved on a mandoline. If you can't find them in your grocery store, they are available online.

HOW
GOOD
FOOD
WORKS
IN THE
KITCHEN

Leaves

CABBAGE, PEACH
AND
PECAN SLAW

Serves 6

Cabbage is an extremely versatile vegetable since it can be sliced, chopped or shredded. It can be eaten raw, sautéed, stewed, pickled or steamed, remaining delicious in any form. It grows in many different colors and usually has a round head with smooth or crinkled leaves. If kept in a very cold refrigerator with low humidity, it can last for four to six months after being harvested.

Ingredients:

Dressing:

2 peaches, peeled, pitted and chopped
2 tablespoons canola oil
½ cup low fat Greek yogurt
2 tablespoons apple cider vinegar
1 teaspoon Dijon mustard
1 teaspoon celery seeds
¼ teaspoon kosher salt
freshly ground black pepper to taste

Slaw:

½ head green and/or red cabbage, finely shredded
3-4 peaches, peeled, pitted and sliced
2 carrots, thinly sliced using a mandoline or y-peeler
1 cup candied pecans (use Candied Nuts recipe on page 260)

Method:

1. Peeling fresh peaches: Make an "x" on the bottom of each peach with a paring knife. Bring a large pot of water to boil. Add 2–3 peaches at a time and boil for 30 seconds to 1 minute (until skin begins to pull away from the "x"). Remove with a slotted spoon and drop into ice water bath. Let cool, dry and remove skin with a paring knife.

2. In a high-powered blender, or food processor, add dressing ingredients blend until smooth.

3. In a large bowl, combine cabbage, peaches, carrots and pecans, and toss with the dressing. Save extra dressing in an airtight container for up to 1 week.

Helpful Tips:

Peaches will ripen faster if you place them in a paper bag at room temperature. But as soon as they are soft, store them in the refrigerator for three to five days.

If peaches are not in season, try using frozen peaches.

CABBAGE, SWEET ONION
AND
PORK STEW

Serves 4–6

Cabbage is one of the oldest cultivated vegetables and has been a part of the human diet for more than 1,000 years. Cabbage heads develop 70–120 days after planting, and their shape can be elongated, pointed or rounded, depending on the variety. Cabbage is a biennial plant, which means that it finishes its life cycle in two years. It is also grown as an ornamental plant, but that variety isn't considered edible.

Ingredients:

2 tablespoons olive oil

1 pound boneless pork tenderloin,
  cut into 1-inch cubes

1 onion, thinly sliced

2 carrots, diced

3 garlic cloves, thinly sliced

1 tablespoon sweet paprika

2 tablespoons finely chopped fresh oregano leaves

1 tablespoon finely chopped fresh mint leaves

1 pound green cabbage,
  cored and chopped (1 small cabbage)

1 can chickpeas (15 ounces), drained and rinsed

½ teaspoon kosher salt

2 cups crushed tomatoes

2 cups water

Method:

1. In a Dutch oven over medium heat, warm oil until hot and shimmery. Add pork and stir frequently, allowing it to brown on all sides, about 3–4 minutes. Remove pork from the Dutch oven and set aside. Add onions and carrots and sauté until onions are lightly browned, about 3–4 minutes. Add garlic, paprika, oregano and mint and sauté until fragrant, about 1–2 minutes.

2. Return pork to the Dutch oven, and stir in cabbage, chickpeas, salt, crushed tomatoes and water. Bring the mixture to a boil and then reduce heat to a simmer. Stir occasionally until the carrots are tender, about 25–30 minutes. Serve hot.

Helpful Tips:

Substitute red cabbage for green cabbage or Cannellini beans for chickpeas for a different look.

Radicchio and Endive Salad

RADICCHIO
AND
ENDIVE
SALAD

Serves 4

Radicchio packs a spicy punch similar to that of radishes. When it is grilled, that punch mellows out. Radicchio grows best during the cooler seasons — spring and fall — and requires full sun to grow the heads, which reach the size of an orange or a grapefruit. Heads are ready to be picked when the leaves are firm, about 60 days after planting. When stored in the refrigerator in a perforated plastic bag, heads can last three to four weeks.

Ingredients:

Dressing:

½ cup olive oil

3 tablespoons sherry vinegar

¼ cup crumbled Gorgonzola cheese

1 teaspoon Dijon mustard

1 teaspoon honey

¼ teaspoon kosher salt

¼ teaspoon freshly ground black pepper

Salad:

1 tablespoon olive oil

2 heads radicchio, cut in half and cores removed

2 heads endive, cores removed and leaves separated

2 sweet apples, cut into ½-inch thick slices

2 pears, cut into ½-inch thick slices

1 cup spiced walnuts (see Spice Mixed Nuts recipe page 260)

¼ cup Pickled Red Onions (see recipe page 204)

Method:

1. Dressing: In a 12-ounce mason jar or similar container, combine olive oil, sherry vinegar, Gorgonzola cheese, Dijon mustard, honey, salt and black pepper. Secure the lid and shake well until incorporated. Set aside.

2. Salad: Heat the grill to medium-high heat. Drizzle olive oil evenly over both sides of the radicchio, endive, apples and pears. Grill radicchio, endive, apples and pears about 2-3 minutes each side until charred and slightly tender. Remove from the heat and let cool.

3. On a large serving platter, place grilled radicchio, apples, pears and endive leaves. Top with spiced walnuts and pickled onions and drizzle the dressing over the salad.

Helpful Tips:

Extra dressing can be stored in the refrigerator for 2 days.

If slicing the pears and apples ahead of time, sprinkle with lemon juice so they don't brown.

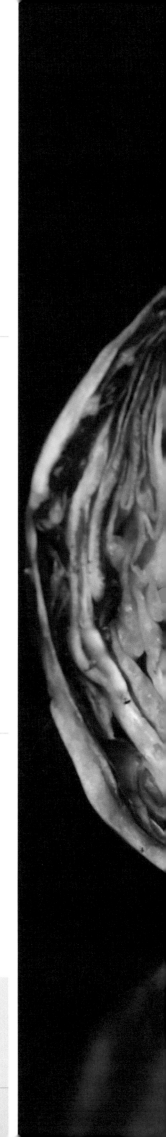

GRILLED ROMAINE LETTUCE
WITH
CRAB

Serves 4-6

Not all lettuce can hold up to being grilled, but romaine, radicchio and endive work well and taste delicious. The secret is to slice the lettuce in half lengthwise, keeping the stem intact so you have a flat side to get the best grill marks possible. Make sure to use a pair of tongs to move the vegetables on the grill and to the serving plate.

Ingredients:

Spicy ranch dressing:

1 avocado, pit removed
½ cup buttermilk
1 tablespoon white vinegar
3 tablespoons mayonnaise
½ teaspoon dried parsley
½ teaspoon dried dill
½ teaspoon onion powder
½ teaspoon garlic powder
¼ teaspoon dried chives
¼ teaspoon unsalted chili powder
¼ teaspoon ground cayenne pepper
¼ teaspoon kosher salt
⅛ teaspoon freshly ground black pepper
water as needed for thinning

Grilled vegetables:

4 corn ears, shucked
2 patty pan squashes, quartered
2 romaine hearts, halved lengthwise
1 tablespoon olive oil

Crab:

12 ounces jumbo lump crabmeat, cartilage removed
1 tablespoon olive oil
1 lemon, juiced
pinch of kosher salt
4 small heirloom tomatoes, quartered
½ cup unsalted sunflower seeds, toasted
¼ cup chopped fresh dill

Method:

1. Spicy ranch dressing: In a blender or food processor, add ingredients and blend until smooth. If dressing is too thick, add a teaspoon of water at a time, blending after each addition until the consistency of a dressing is reached. Set aside.

2. Grilled vegetables: Heat the grill to medium-high heat. Place corn, squash and romaine hearts on a baking pan lined with parchment paper. Drizzle oil evenly over both sides of corn, squash and romaine hearts, then brush or massage the oil to make sure all parts of the vegetables have oil. Next, place the corn and squash on the grill for about 3–4 minutes on each side until charred and slightly tender. Remove and then grill the romaine hearts cut side down for about 1–2 minutes until charred and slightly tender. Remove from the heat and let cool. Remove corn kernels from the cob.

3. Crab: In a small bowl, carefully fold together crab meat with olive oil, lemon juice and salt. Set aside.

4. Salad: On a large serving platter, arrange grilled romaine with corn, squash and tomatoes. Top with crab meat, sunflower seeds and dill. Serve the spicy ranch dressing on the side.

Helpful Tips:

One of the keys to grilling vegetables successfully is making sure they are cut in similar sizes and then working in batches rather than grilling them all at once.

Baby Bok Choy with Mandarin Oranges and Crispy Ramen

BABY BOK CHOY

WITH

MANDARIN ORANGES

AND

CRISPY RAMEN

Serves 4

Bok choy is a relatively new vegetable to the Western world, but it's been cultivated in Asia for thousands of years. It's a mild cabbage that has soft leaves and a crunchy celery-like stalk. Bok choy is versatile, as it can be eaten raw or cooked. The leaves are delicious when tiny, young and tender, and grow best in cool temperatures with partial shade.

Ingredients:

2 teaspoons avocado oil

½ packet ramen noodles,
   broken into small pieces, spice packet discarded

½ cup unsalted raw peanuts

2–3 dried Thai chilis

1 tablespoon sesame oil

3 baby bok choy bulbs, cut in half lengthwise and
   trimmed on the bulb side (both sides should lay
   flat in the pan)

3 green onions, thinly sliced, green parts only

2 garlic cloves, minced

½ cup vegetable broth

2 mandarin oranges,
   peeled and separated into segments

3 tablespoons soy sauce

Method:

1. In a large cast iron pan over low heat, warm the avocado oil until hot and shimmery. Add ramen, peanuts and dried chilis. Stir frequently to prevent burning. When the ramen is toasted, about 8 minutes, remove from the pan and set aside. Wipe the pan clean with a paper towel.

2. In the pan, heat the sesame oil over medium heat until hot and shimmery. Add bok choy cut side down and green onions and garlic to the pan. Sauté until garlic is fragrant, about 1–2 minutes. Add broth, mandarin oranges and soy sauce and continue cooking until bok choy is tender and greens are wilted, about 2–3 minutes. Remove from heat.

3. Top with crispy ramen and peanuts.

Helpful Tips:

It can be difficult to find unflavored ramen noodles at the grocery store, so you can buy any flavored noodle and toss the seasoning included, since our recipe is better than the dried one in the package.

One small can of mandarin oranges can be substituted for fresh ones.

Ramen noodles are made from wheat flour, salt and water but treated with an alkaline mineral water that gives the noodles their yellow hue and springy, chewy texture. They come in a variety of shapes and sizes and can also be made with rice flour.

ARUGULA
AND
TOMATO
SALAD

Serves 4

Arugula was first cultivated in the Mediterranean region and is part of the mustard family. It can easily be grown from a seed in early spring or early fall, and it only takes six to eight weeks to harvest. The young leaves, 2 to 3 inches long, taste best. The white flowers on the plant are also edible, but do not appear until it has bolted, which means the plant is beginning to produce seeds. At that point, the plant should be pulled up or turned under the soil.

Ingredients:

Hot paprika vinaigrette:
¼ cup extra virgin olive oil
2 tablespoons sherry vinegar
1 tablespoon honey
1 shallot, peeled
2 garlic cloves, peeled
½ teaspoon Spanish hot paprika
pinch of kosher salt

Tomatoes and chickpeas:
2 cups cherry tomatoes, assorted colors, sliced in half
1 can chickpeas (15 ounces), drained,
   rinsed and patted dry
2 tablespoons olive oil
1 teaspoon dried oregano
2 tablespoons chopped fresh parsley
kosher salt and freshly ground black pepper to taste

Manchego cheese crisps and salad:
½ cup grated Manchego cheese
3 cups arugula
2 carrots, purple and orange, shredded
½ cup fresh cherries, pitted and quartered
¼ cup green olives, pitted, thinly sliced
¼ cup Marcona almonds, toasted, chopped
1 red apple, thinly sliced and sprinkled with lemon juice
Hot paprika vinaigrette

Method:

1. Hot paprika vinaigrette: In a blender or a food processor, add ingredients and blend until smooth. Set aside.

2. Tomatoes and chickpeas: Preheat oven to 400° and line a baking pan with parchment paper. In a large bowl, add tomatoes and chickpeas and mix with olive oil. Add oregano, parsley, salt and pepper and mix well. Spread seasoned tomatoes and chickpeas evenly on the baking pan, making sure not to overcrowd. Roast in the oven for 15–20 minutes until tomatoes are blistered and lightly browned. Set aside and let cool.

3. Manchego cheese crisps: On a baking pan lined with parchment paper, use a 3 inch metal cookie cutter and place 2 tablespoons of Manchego cheese inside to form a small circle. Repeat the process, leaving plenty of space between each circle. Cook in the oven at 400° until the cheese is toasted and golden brown, about 5–8 minutes. Set aside and let cool before removing.

4. Salad: In a large bowl, combine arugula, carrots, cherries, green olives, almonds, tomatoes, chickpeas and apple slices. Toss salad with hot paprika vinaigrette and garnish with cheese crisps. Store extra dressing in an airtight container in the refrigerator for up to 1 week.

Helpful Tips:

Marcona almonds are sweeter, moister and softer than the classic almond. They're often found in the grocery store with the gourmet cheeses and other elements of a charcuterie board.

KALE
AND
TOFU
SALAD
WITH
GINGER
CARROT
DRESSING
Serves 4

Kale is part of the cabbage family, but it doesn't form a head like round cabbage. Instead, it grows dense, curly bumpy leaves. It's best to plant in the fall and usually takes between 55-75 days from seed to harvest. It's very hardy, and harvest can take place even after the first snowfall. Sunlight is good, but kale will thrive with just a few hours of sunshine a day.

Kale can be very tough and dense, so it requires massaging. We recommend cutting the leaves into bite-size pieces, placing them in a bowl and then using your hands to work the dressing into the leaves, which become softer, tender and easier to eat.

Ingredients:

Ginger carrot dressing:

2 medium carrots, unpeeled

¼ cup rice vinegar

3 tablespoons sesame oil

1 tablespoon honey

1 tablespoon grated, peeled ginger (about ½-inch)

2 teaspoons low-sodium soy sauce

½ teaspoon dried turmeric

¼ cup water, to thin out

Kale and tofu salad:

8 ounces tofu, extra firm, strained, cut into cubes, pressed between paper towels to dry for 15–20 minutes

1 tablespoon low-sodium soy sauce

2 garlic cloves, minced

2 teaspoons sesame oil

½ head green cabbage, shredded

½ head red cabbage, shredded

1 bunch Lacinato kale, leaves chopped, stems finely diced

2 carrots, medium size, shredded

1 red bell pepper, thinly sliced

1 cucumber, thinly sliced

1 cup edamame, frozen, shelled and cooked in the microwave for 1 minute. Let cool.

½ cup unsalted peanuts, roasted and chopped

½ bunch green onions, thinly sliced

Method:

1. Ginger carrot dressing: In a high-powered blender, add ingredients, blend until smooth. Set aside.

2. Tofu: Combine tofu, soy sauce and garlic in a small bowl, stir well. Set aside for about 15 minutes. In a large sauté pan or wok over medium-high heat, warm oil. Remove tofu from the marinade and pat dry with paper towels. Add to the pan in a single layer to allow it to sear for 1–2 minutes. This will prevent the tofu from crumbling. Stir fry until golden, about 3–5 minutes until lightly browned. Remove the pan from heat.

3. Salad: In a large bowl, combine cabbages, kale leaves and stems, carrots, red bell pepper, cucumber and edamame. Toss salad with dressing. Top with tofu, peanuts and green onions.

Helpful Tips:

For frozen kale that lasts 8 to 12 months, blanch leaves and stems. Blanch leaves for 2½ minutes, covering the boiling water pot with a lid to steam-heat floating leaves. Blanch stems for 3 minutes. Place leaves and stems in ice water for 3 minutes. Use a strainer to fish leaves from both boiling and ice water.

Dry leaves by placing them on a towel. Fill the towel with leaves, then roll it up and squeeze to remove excess water. Quick-freeze small clumps of kale individually on a baking pan. After they're frozen, place clumps into freezer bags in bulk. Remove as much air as possible from bags before sealing. When you freeze kale like this, you can grab a handful for a smoothie, or pour out more to create a side dish.

If you don't want to quick-freeze kale, simply place blanched and dried kale into individual packages prior to freezing. Choose the right size freezer bag to suit your serving-size portion. Always remove as much air as possible before sealing bags. A vacuum sealer system works well with kale. Avoid over-packing bags. Flatten bags before sealing to create kale portions that thaw quickly.

If a high-powered blender isn't available, try using a 14.5-ounce can of carrots, drained, in place of fresh for a smoother dressing.

LEAFY VEGGIE
AND
COUSCOUS SALAD

Serves 4

Red and green leaf lettuces are similar in flavor. Red lettuce is earthy and mildly sweet, while green lettuce is crisp with a slight bite. Leaf lettuces don't grow into round heads like many other greens but rather into long, loose leaves that are curly and wrinkled.

Ingredients:

Berbere and tahini dressing:

1 cup green seedless grapes

½ cup fat-free Greek yogurt

2 tablespoons tahini

1 tablespoon olive oil

1 lemon, juice and zest

2 garlic cloves, grated

1 teaspoon berbere spice or garam masala

Pearl couscous and vegetables:

1 tablespoon olive oil

1 onion, diced

2 carrots, diced

2 garlic cloves, diced

1 teaspoon lemon zest

1 cup pearl couscous

¼ cup finely chopped fresh parsley, stems removed

¼ cup dried currants

¼ cup dried apricots, chopped

1 can low-sodium chickpeas (15 ounces),
   drained and rinsed

1¾ cups vegetable broth

½ cup pistachios, toasted and chopped

1 head green leaf lettuce, leaves separated

1 head red leaf lettuce, leaves separated

kosher salt and freshly ground black pepper to taste

Method:

1. Berbere dressing: In a blender, add all ingredients and blend until smooth. Set aside.

2. Couscous: In a medium pot over medium heat, warm oil until hot and shimmery. Add onions and carrots and sauté until golden brown, about 3–4 minutes. Add garlic, lemon zest and couscous and sauté until fragrant and the couscous is toasted, about 1–2 minutes. Add parsley, currants, apricots, chickpeas and broth and bring to a boil. Reduce heat to a simmer, cover the pot with a lid and continue cooking for 10 minutes. Remove from the heat and let stand for an additional 5 minutes. Remove the lid and stir in pistachios.

3. Salad: To serve, plate couscous mixture, lettuces and a spoonful of berbere dressing. Salt and pepper to taste.

Helpful Tips:

Berbere spice is a distinctive blend of seasoning, such as chilis, garlic, ginger, cloves, coriander, allspice and ground cinnamon. If berbere is unavailable at the grocery store, substitute with garam masala.

MUSTARD GREENS
WITH
CRISPY PANCETTA

Serves 4

When shopping for produce, it's easy to confuse mustard greens and collard greens, but they taste completely different. Collard greens are mild, while mustard greens have a sharp, peppery flavor. And yes, yellow mustard, mustard greens and mustard seeds come from the same plant. Avoid slimy, yellow or wilted greens. Mustard greens will keep in the refrigerator for two to three weeks and can be frozen or dried.

Ingredients:

1 tablespoon olive oil

1 ounce pancetta, finely chopped

2 bunches mustard greens, leaves chopped and stems diced

1 garlic clove, thinly sliced lengthwise

1 tablespoon chopped fresh thyme, stems removed

2 tablespoons capers, drained and rinsed

1 tablespoon lemon juice

¼ teaspoon freshly ground black pepper

grated lemon zest

Method:

1. In a large cast iron pan over medium heat, warm oil until hot and shimmery. Add pancetta, stirring frequently. When crispy, remove to a paper towel and set aside.

2. In the pan, add mustard green stems and garlic and sauté until garlic is fragrant, about 1–2 minutes. Then add mustard green leaves and continue cooking until leaves are wilted, about 3–5 minutes. Add thyme, capers, lemon juice and pepper and remove from the heat.

3. Garnish greens with crispy pancetta and lemon zest.

Helpful Tips:

The main difference between pancetta and bacon is that pancetta is cured and dried and bacon is smoked. In cooking, that means bacon is raw and must be cooked before it is eaten, whereas pancetta can be eaten both cooked and uncooked.

Brussels Sprouts with Miso-Glazed Hanger Steak

BRUSSELS SPROUTS
WITH
MISO-GLAZED HANGER STEAK

Serves 4

Brussels sprouts are like mini heads of cabbage. They grow on the sides of thick stalks that can produce about 2 pounds each. The best time of the year to grow them is winter since they become sweeter after the first freeze. Try not to overcook them, as they can produce a strong odor.

Ingredients:

Miso marinade:
½ cup white miso
1 cup mirin
4 garlic cloves, minced
¼ cup soy sauce
2 tablespoons plus 2 teaspoons sesame oil
4 teaspoons chili paste
2 teaspoons cornstarch

Vegetables:
2 tablespoons canola oil
1 pound Brussels sprouts, cut in half
2 carrots, thinly sliced diagonally
  (use rainbow carrots for added color)

Steak:
1 pound hanger steak, trimmed and membrane removed
2 tablespoons canola oil

Garnish:
1 tablespoon sesame seeds

Method:

1. Miso marinade: In a medium bowl, combine miso, mirin, garlic, soy sauce, sesame oil, chili paste and cornstarch and mix well. Set aside about ½ cup of the marinade in a small bowl to use later. Add the steak to the remaining marinade and place in the refrigerator for at least 30 minutes or up to 4 hours.

2. Vegetables: Preheat the oven to 400°. In a large bowl, mix the oil, Brussels sprouts and carrots. Place on a large unlined baking sheet. Roast in the oven for 25–30 minutes until brown.

3. Steak: While vegetables are roasting, prepare the steak. Remove it from the marinade and use a paper towel to pat dry. In a large cast iron skillet over high heat, warm canola oil until hot and shimmery. Add steak and allow a crust to form on one side, about 6–8 minutes, then turn and brown for another 6–8 minutes. Remove and set aside to rest. Cover and keep warm.

4. Marinade sauce: Add the remaining marinade to a small saucepan and warm over medium-low heat for 2-3 minutes. Set aside.

5. Assembly: To plate, slice steak across the grain into ½ inch pieces. Sprinkle meat and vegetables with sesame seeds. Serve the warm sauce on the side.

Helpful Tips:
Extra dressing can be stored in the refrigerator for one week.

BRUSSELS SPROUTS, SQUASH AND SPINACH SALAD

Serves 4

Brussels sprouts are native to northern Europe and get their name from Brussels, Belgium, where they were cultivated in the 16th century. Most production is now in California, where the weather is cool for harvest time that lasts from June to January. More than 80% of the U.S. harvest goes to the frozen food market, but fresh Brussels sprouts will last in the refrigerator for two to four weeks before wilting and turning yellow.

Ingredients:

Squash:

1 pound acorn or delicata squash, seeded,
  halved and cut into ½-inch half-moon slices

2 tablespoons olive oil

1 teaspoon dried oregano

1 teaspoon dried thyme

¼ teaspoon kosher salt

¼ teaspoon freshly ground black pepper

Warm bacon vinaigrette:

2–3 slices bacon strips

2 garlic cloves, minced

1 teaspoon dried thyme

1 teaspoon dried oregano

¼ cup canola oil

3 tablespoons apple cider vinegar

2 tablespoons Dijon mustard

1 tablespoon maple syrup

2 teaspoons smoked paprika

pinch of kosher salt

1 teaspoon cornstarch

¼ cup warm vegetable broth

Salad:

2 cups baby spinach leaves

1 cup Brussels sprouts, shaved (about ½ pound)

½ cup chopped spiced walnuts
  (see Sweet and Spicy Nuts recipe page 260)

¼ cup dried cranberries, unsweetened, chopped

¼ cup crumbled goat cheese

2 tablespoons crumbled bacon

Method:

1. Squash: Preheat the oven to 400° and line a baking pan with parchment paper. In a large bowl, add squash, oil, oregano, thyme, salt and pepper and mix well. Spread seasoned squash evenly on the pan, making sure not to overcrowd. Roast in the oven for 20–25 minutes.

2. Warm bacon vinaigrette: While the squash is in the oven roasting, prepare the dressing. In a 10-inch skillet over medium heat, render bacon until crispy. Remove to a paper towel and set aside. In the skillet with the bacon rendering, sauté garlic, thyme and oregano until fragrant, about 1-2 minutes. Add the canola oil, vinegar, mustard, maple syrup, paprika and salt and bring to a simmer while stirring. In a small bowl, create a slurry by whisking together the cornstarch and warm vegetable broth. Add to the skillet and bring mixture to a boil over medium heat. When the mixture thickens, remove from heat. Set aside and keep warm.

4. Salad: Remove squash from the oven when it is crisp on the outside and tender on the inside. Place in a large bowl, and add spinach, shaved Brussels sprouts, walnuts, cranberries, goat cheese and bacon crumbles. Pour warm vinaigrette over and toss to combine.

Helpful Tips:

We recommend carefully using a mandoline to thinly slice Brussels sprouts.

SIMPLY
ROASTED BRUSSELS SPROUTS

Serves 4

When selecting Brussels sprouts, look for ones that have intact outer leaves and are firm to the touch. Preparation is easy and only requires trimming a very small amount from the knubby end so they don't lose their leaves when roasting. Slice the sprouts lengthwise so the ends are flat to allow them to caramelize. Don't overcrowd the pan, and it's not necessary to turn them midway through roasting. They will develop steam when roasting on their flat side, and the insides will be perfectly tender and the outsides crispy.

Ingredients:

1 pound Brussels sprouts, halved, trimmed on ends still keeping core intact
2 tablespoons olive oil
1 tablespoon minced fresh thyme, stems removed
1 teaspoon minced fresh rosemary, stems removed
½ teaspoon onion powder
½ teaspoon kosher salt
¼ teaspoon freshly ground black pepper

Optional garnish:
2 tablespoons grated Parmesan cheese

Method:

1. Preheat the oven to 400°.

2. In a large bowl, add all ingredients and mix well. Spread seasoned Brussels sprouts evenly, cut side down on an unlined baking pan, making sure not to overcrowd.

3. Roast in the oven for 20–25 minutes until sprouts are tender on the inside and crispy and charred on the outside.

4. Optional: Remove from the oven and sprinkle with Parmesan cheese for extra flavor.

Helpful Tips:

This roasting method can be used for most vegetables.

HOW
GOOD
FOOD
WORKS
IN THE
KITCHEN

Seeds and Legumes

BLACK-EYED PEA CAVIAR
AND
COLLARD GREENS

Serves 4

Black-eyed peas and collard greens are traditional Southern dishes usually cooked with broth, bacon, vinegar and sugar. We give our peas and greens a new look by making them part of a cold salad. They are supposed to bring good luck when eaten on New Year's Day. Collard greens make a great substitute for kale—and if you need to make a salad ahead of time, they'll hold up while sitting in the refrigerator before wilting, even with the dressing on.

Ingredients:

Dressing:

2 tablespoons canola oil

2 tablespoons red wine vinegar

1 teaspoon Dijon mustard

1 teaspoon honey

1 teaspoon finely grated garlic

½ teaspoon Worcestershire sauce

½ teaspoon cayenne pepper

¼ teaspoon kosher salt

Salad:

1 can black-eyed peas (15 ounces), rinsed and drained or 1 bag (12 ounces)
   frozen black-eyed peas, thawed

2 cups collard greens, leaves chiffonaded and stems diced

¼ red onion, diced

2 celery stalks, diced

¼ red bell pepper, diced

¼ orange bell pepper, diced

2 garlic cloves, minced

Method:

1. Dressing: In a mason jar, combine canola oil, red wine vinegar, Dijon mustard, honey, garlic, Worcestershire sauce, cayenne pepper and salt. Secure lid and shake until ingredients are fully incorporated. Set aside.

2. Salad: In a large bowl, add peas, collard greens, red onion, celery, bell peppers and garlic. Add dressing to salad and mix to combine. Store in the refrigerator until ready to serve.

Helpful Tips:

Substitute any dark leafy green for collard greens.

PURPLE HULL PEAS
AND
PORK CHILI

Serves 6–8

Southern peas come in many forms and colors and can easily be substituted. If purple hull peas are unavailable, try using black-eyed peas, crowder peas, cream peas or silver skin peas. Purple hull peas have a pinkish eye, but they taste almost identical to other Southern peas. They are grown extensively throughout Texas and can be produced almost continuously in the warm part of the year.

Tomatillos are the base of most green salsas. These acidic, slightly sweet green fruits originate from Mexico and can be roasted, charred or used raw to make salsas and sauces. This salsa, when added to our pork stew, really kicks it up a level.

Ingredients:

Chili:

2 tablespoons olive oil

1 pork shoulder (about 3 pounds),
   cut into 1-inch cubes

4 garlic cloves, minced

2 carrots, diced

2 cups dried purple hull peas, pre-soaked
   (soak overnight in the refrigerator) or
   2 cans (15 ounces each) purple hull peas,
   rinsed and drained (add canned with salsa)

1 teaspoon smoked paprika

1 teaspoon cumin

1 teaspoon dried oregano

½ teaspoon kosher salt

6 cups vegetable broth

Salsa Verde:

1 pound tomatillos, husks removed

2 poblano peppers, stems removed

2 hatch chilis, stems removed
   or substitute Anaheim peppers

1 onion, peeled and quartered

2 tablespoons olive oil

1 bunch cilantro, stems removed

Garnish:

1 cup assorted pickled vegetables
   (see Zesty Pickled Stems and Shoots recipe page 243)

¼ cup crumbled queso fresco

6–8 pieces of cornbread

Method:

1. Chili: In a large soup pot over medium heat, warm oil until hot and shimmery. Add pork and turn occasionally, allowing the pork to brown on all sides, about 3–4 minutes. Add garlic and carrots and sauté until fragrant, about 1–2 minutes. Stir in peas, smoked paprika, cumin, oregano, salt and vegetable broth. Bring to a boil and reduce heat to a simmer. Cook uncovered on low until pork and peas are tender, about 1–1½ hours. Skim off any foam from the top.

2. Salsa Verde: While the chili is cooking, preheat the oven to broil and line a baking pan with foil. Spread tomatillos, poblano peppers, hatch chilis and onion evenly on the pan and drizzle the mixture with olive oil. Broil in the oven for 5–8 minutes, turning over halfway, until tomatillos and peppers are charred. Keep a close eye on them while broiling. Set aside and let cool for about 10 minutes. Transfer mixture and cilantro to a blender and blend until smooth. Add about 2 cups Salsa Verde into pork and peas, bring to a boil and then reduce heat to a simmer. Taste and adjust seasoning if needed.

3. To serve: Top each bowl of chili with pickled vegetables, queso fresco and a slice of cornbread.

Helpful Tips:

Queso fresco is a white cheese made with a combination of goat and cow's milk. It will soften up when heated, but it doesn't melt like mozzarella.

Store the extra Salsa Verde in the refrigerator and serve with tortilla chips.

MOM'S LIMA BEANS

Serves 4–6

Lima beans are also known as butter beans and come in two varieties — baby limas and fordhooks. If you are planting lima beans in your garden, you'll need to know which variety to plant. One needs a trellis for support so the beans can climb up and grow. The other variety grows in a bush and does not need support. The beans will take 65 to 75 days from seed to harvest. They are commonly used in soups and stews.

Ingredients:

2 tablespoons olive oil

4 ounces frozen pearl onions

1 smoked ham hock (medium size)

2 garlic cloves, minced

2 cups lima beans, fresh or frozen

1 bay leaf

1 teaspoon smoked paprika

¼ bunch fresh oregano, chopped

½ teaspoon kosher salt

4 cups vegetable broth

Method:

1. In a medium soup pot over medium heat, warm oil until hot and shimmery. Add pearl onions and sauté until lightly browned, about 2–3 minutes. Add ham hock and stir frequently, allowing the pork to brown on all sides, about 3–4 minutes. Add garlic and lima beans and sauté until fragrant, about 1–2 minutes. Stir in bay leaf, smoked paprika, oregano, salt and vegetable broth. Bring to a boil and then reduce heat to a simmer.

2. Cook uncovered on low until beans are tender, about 20–25 minutes. Remove the meat from the ham hock and add to the soup. Before serving, remove the bay leaf.

Helpful Tips:

We don't recommend eating raw legumes. Beans contain a compound called lectin which isn't easily digested. Cooking neutralizes lectins and improves their taste.

Fava Bean Puree with Lamp Chops

FAVA BEAN PUREE
WITH
LAMB CHOPS

Serves 4

Fresh fava beans are usually bountiful in the spring, but are found dried year round. To buy them fresh, look for large, long beans (larger than a regular green bean) that have flat, oval, sweet pods inside. The outside bean is not edible, so you need to "unzip" it with a knife and gently push out the pods. When cooked, these delicious legumes are sweet, flavorful and a perfect match for lamb. Our tabbouleh has a secret ingredient — Aleppo pepper, a spice that originated in the Middle East and adds an earthy, fruity flavor. If it is unavailable at your grocery store, try substituting with sweet paprika and a pinch of cayenne pepper.

Ingredients:

Tabbouleh salad:

½ cup fine bulgur wheat

1 cup water

3 tablespoons extra virgin olive oil

1½ lemons, juice and zest

2 garlic cloves, minced

¼ teaspoon kosher salt

¼ teaspoon ground Aleppo pepper

2–3 bunches fresh parsley,
   stems removed and chopped (about 2 cups)

1 bunch fresh mint, stems removed and chopped

3 heirloom tomatoes (about ½ pound),
   seeds removed and diced

2 medium cucumbers, diced

¼ bunch green onions, thinly sliced

½ cup pine nuts, toasted

Fava bean puree:

2 cups fava beans, shelled and cooked
   (substitute canned if unavailable fresh)

2 garlic cloves, minced

2 tablespoons fresh dill, stems removed

1 tablespoon lemon juice

½ teaspoon ground turmeric

¼ teaspoon kosher salt

⅓ cup olive oil

¼ cup vegetable broth

Lamb chops:

1 rack of lamb (about 2 pounds), French trimmed, 8 rib chops

¼ teaspoon kosher salt

2 tablespoons olive oil, divided

¼ cup panko bread crumbs

1 tablespoon Dijon mustard

2 garlic cloves, minced

2 tablespoons finely chopped fresh parsley, stems removed

1 tablespoon finely chopped fresh dill, stems removed

1 tablespoon finely chopped fresh rosemary, stems removed

1 teaspoon Harissa Spice Blend (see recipe page 254)

½ teaspoon ground turmeric

Garnish:

1 tablespoon Turmeric Oil (see Turmeric and Ginger Oil recipe page 262)

Helpful Tips:

If using a coarse bulgur, combine water and bulgur over high heat and bring to a boil. Reduce heat to a simmer, cover and cook until bulgur is tender but not mushy, about 8–10 minutes. Drain off excess water and fluff with a fork. Set aside to cool.

Method:

1. Tabbouleh Salad: In a medium bowl, combine bulgur and water and let soak for about 20–25 minutes or until it fluffs. Drain off excess liquid. Stir in olive oil, lemon juice, lemon zest, garlic, salt and Aleppo pepper. Stir in parsley, mint, tomatoes, cucumber, green onions and pine nuts. Refrigerate 1 hour before serving.

2. Fava Bean Puree: In a food processor, place the fava beans, garlic, dill, lemon juice, turmeric and salt, then blend. Slowly add olive oil in a steady stream until you achieve a smooth purée, stopping to clean the edges of the food processor as needed. Slowly add broth until puree reaches a hummus-like consistency. Set aside.

3. Roasted Lamb: Preheat oven to 450°. Season lamb with salt. In a large sauté pan over medium heat, warm 1 tablespoon of oil until hot and shimmery. Add lamb and allow to sear for about 1 minute before turning to the other side. Once seared on both sides, set on a roasting pan. In a small bowl, combine remaining 1 tablespoon olive oil, panko bread crumbs, mustard, garlic, parsley, dill, rosemary, harissa and turmeric. Spread mixture evenly over the rack of lamb. Roast in the oven for 20–25 minutes until the lamb reaches an internal temperature of 135°. Let rest about 10 minutes before carving.

4. To plate: Serve 2 lamb chops over tabbouleh with a spoonful of fava bean puree. Garnish with a drizzle of turmeric oil.

STOVETOP
GREEN
BEANS

Serves 4

There are over 130 varieties of green beans, and they have all kinds of names — French beans, string beans, snap beans and haricot verts, for example. We recommend trimming the ends by snapping off the stems, or you can line them up on a cutting board and trim them in groups. Fresh green beans will last about seven days in the refrigerator if you keep them in a sealed plastic bag but will last several months in the freezer.

Ingredients:

Sauce:

2 tablespoons whole wheat flour

1 cup vegetable broth

½ cup whole milk

2 tablespoons minced fresh thyme, stems removed

½ teaspoon kosher salt

¼ teaspoon freshly ground black pepper

Green beans:

1 tablespoon olive oil

½ sweet onion, thinly sliced

4 ounces cremini or button mushrooms, thinly sliced

5 garlic cloves, minced

1 pound green beans, ends trimmed

¼ cup grated Parmesan cheese

¼ cup whole wheat panko bread crumbs, toasted

Method:

1. In a small bowl, combine the sauce ingredients. Mix well and set aside.

2. In a large cast iron pan over medium heat, add oil and heat it until hot and shimmery. Add onions and sauté until lightly browned, about 2–3 minutes. Add mushrooms and garlic and continue to sauté until mushrooms are tender, about 3–4 minutes. Add green beans and continue to cook for another 2–4 minutes.

3. Add sauce mixture and bring to a boil, stirring frequently to prevent sauce from burning. Reduce heat to a simmer and cook green beans until they are tender and the sauce is thickened, about 15–20 minutes.

4. Remove from the heat and top with Parmesan cheese and bread crumbs.

Helpful Tips:

Substitute 2 teaspoons of dried thyme for fresh thyme.

Roasted Corn with Garlic Lime Mayo

ROASTED CORN
WITH
GARLIC LIME MAYO

Serves 4

Fresh corn is often called the perfect summer vegetable. It comes off the stalk sweet, juicy and ready to be eaten raw, but roasting or grilling adds another dimension to its taste. Sweet corn can be grown with yellow, white or bicolor yellow-and-white kernels and can stay sweet after harvest longer than other corn varieties. Corn has become a staple in many parts of the world since it can be transformed into a variety of different products including flour, popcorn, cornstarch and cornmeal. It's also pressed and turned into a liquid that is used to make corn syrup, corn oil and alcoholic beverages such as bourbon whiskey.

Ingredients:

Corn:

3 tablespoons light mayonnaise

2 tablespoons Greek yogurt or sour cream

2 garlic cloves, finely grated

2 teaspoons Southwest Spice Blend
  (see recipe page 254)

¼ teaspoon kosher salt

½ lime, juiced

¼ bunch fresh cilantro, chopped and divided,
  stems removed

4 corn ears, shucked and cleaned

Garnish:

¼ cup grated cotija cheese

1 lime, cut into wedges

Method:

1. Preheat the oven to 400° and line a baking pan with parchment paper.

2. In a small bowl, combine mayonnaise, yogurt, garlic, Southwest Spice Blend, salt, lime juice and half of the chopped cilantro.

3. Place corn on the pan and spread about 2 teaspoons of the garlic mayo mixture over each ear. Roast in the oven for 15–18 minutes until the corn is lightly charred on the outside and tender.

4. Before serving, garnish roasted corn with remaining garlic mayo, cilantro, cheese and lime wedges.

Helpful Tips:

Cotija cheese and queso fresco are both mild, slightly salty Mexican cheeses which can be substituted for each other in recipes.

CORN
AND
EDAMAME
SUCCOTASH
WITH
FLANK
STEAK

Serves 4

Succotash is an American dish that traditionally consists of corn and lima beans. In our succotash, we utilize edamame in place of lima beans. Edamame is very easy to grow, especially in warm climates, and takes between 90 and 150 days from seed to harvest. It's ready when the pods are bright green, filled with plump seeds and at least 2–3 inches long. Edamame should be cooked before you eat it since it's a soy product and cannot be digested raw. Soy contains a trypsin inhibitor which is an enzyme needed to properly digest protein. Cooking destroys the trypsin inhibitor.

Ingredients:

Marinade:

2 tablespoons unsalted raw peanuts

1 tablespoon fish sauce

2 limes, zest and juice

4 garlic cloves, peeled

½ bunch fresh cilantro, stems removed

½ bunch fresh mint, stems removed

1 tablespoon honey

1 teaspoon chili paste

½ teaspoon instant coffee

Steak:

1 pound flank steak, scored

1 tablespoon avocado oil

Succotash:

1 onion, diced

3 garlic cloves, minced

1 carrot, diced

kernels from 1 ear fresh corn

1 summer squash, diced

1 zucchini, diced

1 bell pepper, diced

1 cup frozen edamame, shelled and thawed

1 tablespoon fish sauce

1 tablespoon chili paste

1 tablespoon honey

2 teaspoons sesame oil

1 tablespoon chopped fresh cilantro

1 tablespoon chopped fresh mint

¼ cup unsalted peanuts, toasted and chopped

Method:

1. Marinade: In a blender, add all ingredients and blend until smooth. Place steak in a plastic bag (or small bowl), cover with marinade and mix well. Place in the refrigerator and let marinate for at least 2 hours or overnight. Remove and let the marinated meat sit at room temperature about 30 minutes before cooking.

2. Steak: In a large sauté pan over medium heat, warm the oil until hot and shimmery. Add the steak and sear until golden brown, about 3–4 minutes. Using tongs, gently turn the steak to the other side and continue cooking for another 3–4 minutes until it reaches the desired temperature. Remove from the pan and let rest for 5–10 minutes.

3. Succotash: In the same sauté pan, add onions and garlic and sauté until garlic is fragrant, about 1–2 minutes. Add carrots, corn, squash, zucchini, bell pepper and edamame and continue cooking, stirring frequently until vegetables are lightly browned, about 5–6 minutes. Stir in fish sauce, chili paste, honey and sesame oil and continue cooking until vegetables are tender and the sauce forms a glaze, about 2–3 minutes. Remove from the heat and stir in cilantro, mint and peanuts.

4. Serving: Thinly slice steak on the diagonal and serve with a portion of succotash.

Helpful Tips:

Frozen edamame can be quickly defrosted in the microwave or run under cold water before adding to the recipe.

BLACK BEAN BLENDED BURGERS

Yields 4 6-ounce patties

Black beans are incredibly easy to grow — just give them water and sunshine. They can be grown in the ground or in containers, but they need a trellis, stake or other means of support to keep them off the ground. They do best in warm weather, so plant them in late spring. The beans will germinate in 10–14 days and will reach maturity for harvest in about 100 days.

Mushrooms aren't a vegetable or a fruit but a tasty, edible fungi. They can resemble meat with a similar texture and umami flavor when cooked.

Ingredients:

4 ounces cremini mushrooms
1 tablespoon canola oil
1 cup black beans (½ of a 15-ounce can), drained and rinsed
12 ounces ground beef, 90/10
1 teaspoon Worcestershire sauce
2 teaspoons Grilling Seasoning Blend (see recipe page 254)
1 teaspoon kosher salt

Method:

1. Burger patties: In a food processor, place mushrooms and pulse until they resemble ground beef. In a large skillet over medium heat, warm oil until hot and shimmery. Add mushrooms and sauté until moisture is reduced by half, about 7–8 minutes. Remove from heat and let cool.

2. In a medium bowl, add black beans and crush them with a fork. Add cooked mushrooms, ground beef, Worcestershire, Grilling Seasoning Blend and salt and mix thoroughly. Portion into 4 equal-sized patties.

3. Grilled burgers: Heat grill to medium heat and grill burgers for about 3–4 minutes on each side until internal temperature reaches 155°. Flip only once to make sure the burgers do not break apart.

4. Serve burger with favorite toppings on a toasted bun.

Helpful Tips:

If no outdoor grill is available, use an oven-ready grill pan or skillet and sear to get grill marks and then place in a 400° oven for 15 minutes or until the temperature reaches at least 155°.

CHOCOLATE S'MORES HUMMUS

Serves 6–8

This dessert will be a favorite of children and adults alike. Hummus is basically any white or black bean that is blended into a thick paste and then seasoned with a variety of spices, but it can also have sugar and chocolate added to make it a dessert. It's very easy and can be prepared ahead of time and then toasted in the oven until the marshmallows brown on top. We also recommend serving this with fresh fruit.

Ingredients:

Simple syrup:
½ cup brown sugar
½ cup water

Chocolate mixture:
2 cans chickpeas (15 ounces each),
   drained and rinsed
½ cup unsweetened cocoa powder
½ cup simple syrup
⅓ cup canola oil
¼ teaspoon kosher salt
½ cup water for thinning, if needed

Marshmallow topping:
1 cup pecans, toasted, unsalted and chopped
1 cup graham cracker crumbles
½ cup semi-sweet chocolate chips
2 cups mini marshmallows
apple slices or pear slices

Method:

1. Simple syrup: Heat the water in a small saucepan over medium-low heat until hot (do not bring to a boil). Add brown sugar and stir until fully dissolved. Remove from the heat and let cool to room temperature before using or storing.

2. Chocolate mixture: In a food processor, combine chickpeas, cocoa powder, simple syrup, oil and salt. Blend until smooth, stopping to clean the edges of the food processor as needed. Add water, a teaspoon at a time, until it reaches the desired consistency.

3. Marshmallow topping: Preheat the oven to 375°. Grease 8 small dishes or an 8x8 baking pan. Spread the chocolate mixture evenly in the prepared dishes. Top with pecans, graham cracker crumbles and chocolate chips and lightly press into the chocolate mixture. Evenly distribute marshmallows over the chocolate mixture. Transfer pan to the oven and bake for 12–15 minutes or until the marshmallows are evenly toasted. Serve with apple or pear slices.

Helpful Tips:

For a smoother chocolate consistency, drain and rinse chickpeas. Add to a small bowl and combine with 3 tablespoons cornstarch. In a small skillet, heat the chickpeas until warm. Remove and place back in the bowl. Cover the chickpeas with water and rub them together with your hands to remove the skins. The skins will float to the top. Rinse and repeat several times until most of the skins are gone.

HOW
GOOD
FOOD
WORKS
IN THE
KITCHEN

Roots

SHAVED RADISH SALAD
AND
TURMERIC VINAIGRETTE

Serves 4

Radishes are one of the easiest root vegetables to grow, and also one of the fastest. They go from seed to harvest in as little as three weeks. The best radishes are planted in the early spring or fall, as they need cool soil to flourish. And it's good that radishes grow quickly, since one radish seed produces only one radish plant, and one radish plant produces only one radish. Once the radishes have been harvested and their tops trimmed, they can be stored in the refrigerator for 4–6 weeks.

Ingredients:

Turmeric vinaigrette:

1-inch turmeric root, peeled and grated
   or ½ teaspoon ground turmeric
½ cup extra virgin olive oil
2 tablespoons white balsamic vinegar
1 tablespoon lemon juice
1 tablespoon honey
½ teaspoon whole grain mustard
¼ teaspoon kosher salt

Radish salad:

6–8 radishes (globe, watermelon or
   any other radishes), washed and unpeeled
2–3 rainbow carrots, washed and unpeeled
1 golden beet, washed and unpeeled
¼ cup fresh mint leaves, stems removed
¼ cup chopped fresh dill, stems removed
½ cup chopped candied pecans
   (see Candied Nuts recipe on page 260)

Method:

1. Turmeric vinaigrette: In a 12-ounce jar or similar container, combine all ingredients. Secure the lid and shake well. Set aside.

2. Radish salad: Using a mandoline slicer, thinly slice radishes, carrots and beets lengthwise.

3. In a large bowl, combine vegetables, mint leaves, dill and candied pecans.

4. Drizzle 2 or 3 tablespoons of turmeric vinaigrette over the salad. Serve chilled. The remaining dressing can be stored in the refrigerator for up to a week.

Helpful Tips:

To thinly slice the radishes, beets and carrots, use a mandoline, y-peeler or the large-hole side of a box grater. Take your time and go slowly while using a mandoline. We recommend using your palm to push the vegetables through it so as not to cut a finger while slicing. Grated vegetables will produce a different "look" but they'll be just as tasty!

Radishes with Lemon Thyme Butter

RADISHES
WITH
LEMON
THYME
BUTTER

Serves 4

Once widely used across Europe as an appetite stimulant, radishes have a crisp and peppery bite that can brighten up any dish. They come in an array of colors, sizes and spice levels, so don't be afraid to try some different varieties in this recipe. The most common in the United States is the red globe radish. Sautéing or pan-roasting radishes allows them to develop a milder, smooth flavor and texture that is enhanced by tangy lemon juice and fragrant thyme. As is the case with most root vegetables, make sure to save the leafy green radish tops to use later in a pesto, stir fry or salad.

Ingredients:

1 tablespoon unsalted butter

1 tablespoon canola oil

2 large shallots, cut into quarters

1 pound of mixed radish varieties, unpeeled, washed and quartered

1 tablespoon minced fresh thyme, stems removed

1 tablespoon lemon juice

1 lemon, zest

2 tablespoons white wine

½ teaspoon freshly ground black pepper

½ teaspoon kosher salt

Garnish:
additional fresh thyme and lemon wedges

Method:

1. In a large cast iron skillet over medium heat, warm the butter and oil until hot and shimmery.

2. Add shallots and sauté until lightly browned, about 3–5 minutes. Add radishes and thyme and continue cooking, stirring frequently until radishes are golden and tender, about 10–12 minutes. Stir in lemon juice, zest, white wine, pepper and salt.

3. Garnish with additional thyme sprigs and lemon wedges before serving.

Helpful Tips:

In this dish, the radishes can also be roasted in the oven at 400° for 20–25 minutes until they are soft and golden brown.

BRAISED PARSNIPS
AND
PEARS

Serves 4

Much like carrots, parsnips grow best in the winter months and have a slightly sweet and woody taste with a creamy texture when cooked. But unlike carrots, they can become tough and chewy when dry-roasted, so the braising method used in this recipe keeps them deliciously moist and tender. The parsnip's perfect partner in this dish is the Anjou pear, which has a firm texture and mild, citrusy flavor.

Ingredients:

2 tablespoons olive oil

½ sweet onion, minced

2 Anjou pears, halved

1 garlic clove, minced

1 pound parsnips, unpeeled, washed, tops trimmed
    and cut lengthwise into ½-inch pieces

1 tablespoon chopped fresh dill, stems removed

½ teaspoon smoked paprika

½ teaspoon kosher salt

¼ teaspoon freshly ground black pepper

1½ cups vegetable broth

2 tablespoons white balsamic vinegar

1 tablespoon maple syrup

chopped fresh dill

Method:

1. Preheat the oven to 425°.

2. In a large cast iron skillet over medium heat, warm oil until hot and shimmery.

3. Place the pears in the skillet with the cut side down and allow to brown for 3–5 minutes. Remove the pears to a plate and set aside.

4. To the skillet, add onion, garlic, parsnips, dill, paprika, salt and pepper and sauté until garlic is fragrant and parsnips begin to brown, about 3–4 minutes. Add the broth and pears back to the pan, browned side up.

5. Drizzle the vinegar and syrup on top and roast in the oven for 20–30 minutes.

6. When parsnips and pears are fork tender, remove and garnish with fresh dill.

Helpful Tips:

Early picked parsnips have tender cores that can be eaten raw, but larger parsnips have woody, tough cores that need to be cut out before cooking.

Add fruit to roasted dishes to increase sweetness without adding additional sugar.

Peeling vegetables is not necessary. Just make sure they are clean.

ROASTED PARSNIPS
AND
STEWED CHICKEN

Serves 4

This parsnip and stewed chicken dish is a hearty meal that is sure to warm you up during the cold winter months. While you can find parsnips year-round in the grocery store, they're at their absolute best in the dead of winter, when frost converts the vegetable's starch to sugar. Small parsnips don't need peeling — just scrub clean and cook. Although, if they're older, they should be peeled; the central core is very fibrous and should be cut away.

Ingredients:

Chicken:

4 chicken thighs, bone-in with skin, excess fat trimmed
   (about 1¼ pounds)
pinch of salt
1 teaspoon ancho chili powder
1 tablespoon olive oil

Vegetables:

1 white or yellow onion, diced
2 celery stalks, diced
4 garlic cloves, minced
1 pound small parsnips, washed and unpeeled,
   tops trimmed and cut into equal-sized pieces
½ pound heirloom carrots, washed and unpeeled,
   cut into equal-sized pieces
5–6 radishes, washed and unpeeled
½ teaspoon ancho chili powder
1 teaspoon dried oregano
1 teaspoon unsweetened cocoa powder
1 teaspoon cumin
½ teaspoon kosher salt
2 cups low-sodium vegetable broth
1 lime, zest and juice
¼ bunch fresh cilantro, chopped, stems removed
1 cup unsalted peanuts, roasted and chopped
¼ red onion, thinly sliced
4–8 whole grain corn tortillas
1 cup shaved purple cabbage
Hatch Chili Cream (see recipe page 258)

Method:

1. Chicken: Season chicken thighs with a pinch of salt and ancho chili powder. In a Dutch oven over medium heat, warm the oil until hot and shimmery. Add chicken thighs and allow to sear for about 6–8 minutes before turning to the other side. Once browned, remove and set aside.

2. Vegetables: In the Dutch oven, add onions and celery and sauté until lightly browned, about 3–4 minutes. Add garlic, parsnips, carrots and radishes and sauté until the garlic is fragrant, about 1–2 minutes. Stir in ancho chili powder, oregano, cocoa powder, cumin and salt. Return chicken thighs to the pot and add vegetable broth. Cover with the lid and cook for 20–25 minutes until parsnips, carrots and radishes are tender on the inside and the chicken has an internal temperature of 165°.

3. Remove from the heat and stir in lime zest and juice, cilantro, peanuts and onions.

4. Assemble: Remove skin and shred chicken thighs using 2 forks and serve on a warm tortilla with some of the vegetables, shredded cabbage and Hatch Chili Cream.

Helpful Tips:

Unsweetened cocoa powder blended with chili peppers adds an intense, smoky and spicy flavor to proteins like chicken, pork and beef.

CARAMELIZED BABY TURNIPS
AND
GREENS

Serves 4

Turnips are in season during the cooler months because warmer weather causes them to become stringy, tough and too intensely flavored. They usually have white or slightly yellow flesh, but they can also be purple, green or mottled. The yellow-fleshed turnips are hardier than the others, making them favorable for roasting. Purple and green turnips are often shaved and eaten raw. Picking turnips when they are young ensures that the roots and greens are tender, sweet and mild, making them perfect for charring, sautéing and roasting.

Ingredients:

1 tablespoon canola oil

1½ pounds baby turnips with greens (about 6–8),
   unpeeled, washed and quartered with their green
   tops roughly chopped

2 garlic cloves, thinly sliced lengthwise

1 teaspoon dried thyme

1 tablespoon unsalted butter

1 cup low-sodium vegetable broth

1 tablespoon apple cider vinegar

2 teaspoons honey

1 teaspoon smoked paprika

½ teaspoon kosher salt

¼ teaspoon freshly ground black pepper

Method:

1. In a large cast iron skillet over medium heat, warm the oil until hot and shimmery.

2. Add turnips and allow to brown before stirring, about 2–3 minutes. Add garlic, thyme and butter and sauté until the garlic is fragrant, about 4–5 minutes. Stir frequently.

3. Stir in broth, vinegar, honey, smoked paprika, salt and pepper and continue cooking uncovered until turnips are tender, about 4–5 minutes. Add turnip greens and continue cooking until liquid is reduced by half, about 20–25 minutes.

4. Serve turnips and greens with broth.

Helpful Tips:

If baby turnips with greens aren't available, substitute with white turnips and Swiss chard leaves.

ROOT VEGETABLES
WITH
SOUTHWEST PORK

Serves 4

Root vegetables are the star of this deliciously easy one-pot recipe. Root vegetables are believed to be relics of primitive agriculture, as they can be traced back to ancient times. Carrots and parsnips both belong to the Apiaceae family. Many historians believe carrots originated from either Afghanistan or Turkey and were first cultivated as a food crop in the 10th century, while parsnips date back to Germany in 1542.

Ingredients:

Tenderloin:

1 pork tenderloin (about 1¼ pounds)

1 tablespoon canola oil

1 teaspoon smoked sweet paprika

1 teaspoon Southwest Spice Blend
   (see recipe page 254)

½ teaspoon kosher salt

Vegetables:

2 pounds of root vegetables
   (carrots, turnips and beets), washed and unpeeled,
   cut into equal-sized pieces

3 tablespoons canola oil

1 tablespoon smoked sweet paprika

1 teaspoon Southwest Spice Blend
   (see recipe page 254)

1 teaspoon dried oregano

½ teaspoon kosher salt

Creamy Chimichurri sauce (see recipe page 257)

Method:

1. Preheat the oven to 400°. Pat tenderloin dry with a paper towel and trim away excess fat and silverskin.

2. In a large Dutch oven over medium-high heat, warm oil until hot and shimmery. Add tenderloin and allow to sear for about 1 minute before rotating to the other side. Be patient: the tenderloin will unstick when the crust forms from searing. Continue turning so all sides are browned. Place tenderloin in a baking pan and season with smoked paprika, Southwest Spice Blend and salt. Set aside.

3. In a large bowl, add cut root vegetables and mix with oil. Add remaining seasonings and toss well.

4. Place seasoned vegetables evenly around the pork tenderloin in the pan.

5. Roast in the oven for 20–25 minutes until the pork reaches an internal temperature of 145°. Remove tenderloin when ready and allow to rest 5–10 minutes while vegetables continue cooking until they are crisp on the outside and tender on the inside.

6. Slice pork into pieces. Serve with vegetables and Creamy Chimichurri sauce on the side.

Helpful Tips:

To remove the silverskin (tough, white connective tissue), use the tip of the knife to cut a small piece of the silverskin. Next, grab hold of the small tab of silverskin while simultaneously pushing the knife horizontally along the length of the tenderloin so it peels off easily. Make sure to angle the blade away from you and repeat the process if needed.

Honey Pecan Sweet Potato Hash

HONEY PECAN SWEET POTATO HASH

Serves 4

In many supermarkets, sweet potatoes are mistakenly labeled as yams. Yams have a black or brown bark-like skin, are starchier and drier than the average sweet potato and are often hard to find in typical American grocery stores. The skin of sweet potatoes contains fiber and nutrients and is completely edible, so there's no need to peel them before cooking — just wash them well.

Ingredients:

2 tablespoons canola oil

1 pound sweet potatoes
  (about 2 medium purple and gold), washed,
  unpeeled and cut into small cubes

½ white onion, diced

1 cup diced bell peppers (mixed colors)

2 garlic cloves, minced

1 tablespoon tomato paste

1 tablespoon finely chopped fresh thyme,
  stems removed

1 tablespoon finely chopped fresh sage,
  stems removed

1 teaspoon chili powder

½ teaspoon smoked paprika

¼ teaspoon ground cinnamon

½ teaspoon kosher salt

¼ teaspoon freshly ground black pepper

½ cup low-sodium vegetable broth

2 tablespoons honey

1 cup kale, torn

½ cup unsalted pecans, toasted and chopped

4 large eggs

Method:

1. In a large cast iron pan over medium heat, warm oil until hot and shimmery. Add sweet potatoes and sauté, about 2–3 minutes, stirring occasionally to prevent burning. Add onions, bell peppers, garlic and tomato paste and sauté until lightly browned, about 1–2 minutes. Add thyme, sage, chili powder, smoked paprika, cinnamon, salt, pepper, broth and honey and cook until the sweet potatoes are tender and the liquid has thickened into a glaze, about 15–20 minutes. Remove the pan from the heat. Gently mix in kale and toasted pecans.

2. Preheat the oven to broil.

3. Using a spoon, create four well indentations in the sweet potato mixture and carefully crack an egg into each one. Place under the broiler and cook the eggs until they are set but the yellow is still runny, about 3 minutes. Serve immediately.

Helpful Tips:

The honey in our hash helps to round out the flavors, balancing the bitterness from the kale and the heat from the spices, while the eggs add a creaminess tying the whole dish together.

HARISSA SPICED SWEET POTATOES

Serves 4

Sweet potatoes are the most common warm season root vegetables in the southern United States. They aren't grown from seeds like most other vegetables, but are propagated by growing transplants from the roots of other sweet potatoes. These sprouts are called "slips," which develop roots and become complete plants in about six weeks. After the sweet potato slips have matured in the soil for four to five months, they are ready for harvesting. They are very sensitive to frost, so they should be planted in late spring.

Ingredients:

½ lemon, zest and juice
¼ cup dried apricots, diced
1 pound sweet potatoes, washed, unpeeled, cut lengthwise into equal-sized wedges
2 tablespoons olive oil
1 teaspoon Harissa Spice Blend (see recipe page 254)
½ teaspoon kosher salt
½ cup unsalted pistachios, toasted and chopped

Method:

1. Preheat the oven to 400° and line a baking pan with parchment paper.

2. In a small bowl, combine lemon zest, juice and apricots. Set aside.

3. In a large bowl, add sweet potatoes and mix with olive oil, Harissa Spice Blend and salt.

4. Spread seasoned sweet potatoes evenly on the baking pan, making sure not to overcrowd. Roast in the oven for 15 minutes, then remove and top with the apricot mixture. Return to the oven for 10–15 minutes until potatoes are crisp on the outside and tender on the inside. Sprinkle with chopped pistachios before serving.

Helpful Tips:

Try substituting any root vegetable for sweet potatoes with this recipe and adjust the cooking time if needed.

If you don't have time to make the Harissa Spice Blend, it can be found in the seasoning section of the grocery store.

Sweet potatoes can also be cut into slices or cubes, but adjust the cooking time.

CARROTS
WITH A
KICK

Serves 4

Carrots are the Swiss army knife of vegetables — the most versatile ingredient in the vegetable kingdom. They are used in cuisines around the world and hold up well in just about every cooking method. With a storage time of up to two weeks in the refrigerator and many uses for the leafy green tops, carrots make a great addition to almost every vegetable dish. If you have planted carrots in your garden, gently pull them from the soil when the width of the carrot attached to the leafy greens reaches roughly 3/4 inch. When selecting carrots at the grocery store, choose ones that are firm and bright in color without cracks or blemishes. Carrot skins contain fiber and nutrients, so you do not need to peel them. That means less time prepping and more time enjoying what you create.

Ingredients:

1 pound carrots, unpeeled, washed and cut into equal-sized pieces
2 tablespoons unsalted butter or olive oil
1 tablespoon water
1 teaspoon low-sodium Tajin seasoning

Method:

1. In a microwave-safe bowl, add all ingredients and mix well.

2. Cover loosely with a lid or a damp paper towel.

3. Cook on high in the microwave for 3 minutes. Check carrots for desired doneness. Continue cooking in 1 minute intervals until carrots reach desired texture.

4. Stir well before serving to evenly coat carrots with seasoning.

Helpful Tips:

For an extra-easy side dish on a busy school night, a bag of baby carrots can be substituted.

Tajin spice is a blend of chili peppers, sea salt and dehydrated lime juice. The powder has a tangy, spicy flavor and is commonly used to give vegetables and fruits a kick.

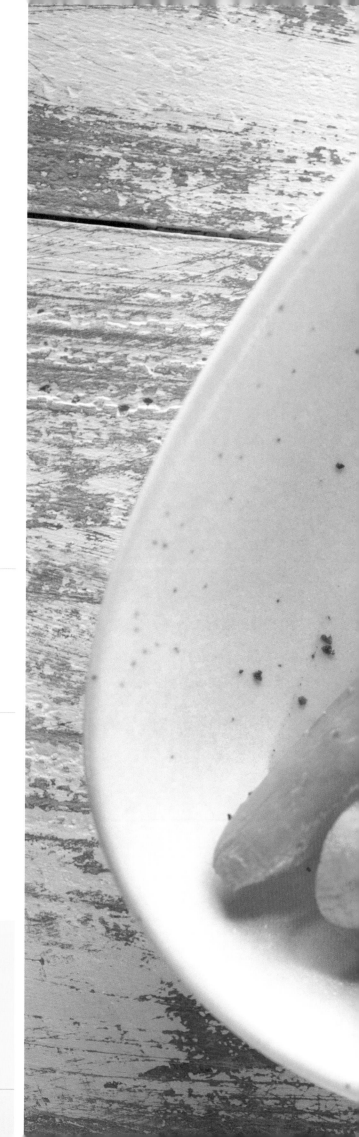

SPICED BEETS AND CITRUS LENTILS

Serves 4

Beets come in many varieties, and the golden beets used in this protein-rich lentil recipe have a bright yellow color and a sweet, earthy taste. Beets are a root vegetable that grow in cool weather and are ready to harvest seven to eight weeks after planting, when their diameter is 1 to 3 inches. Whether you get your beets from a garden or the supermarket, store them in an airtight container or plastic bag in the refrigerator. The beets will keep for one to two weeks, and the tops will keep for up to three days. For this dish, we only cook the dense root portion of the beet, but save the leafy-green tops to use in a stir fry, omelet or home-style side dish. Garam Masala Blend enhances the sweetness of the beets and adds a touch of spice.

Ingredients:

Beets

2 golden beets, scrubbed clean,
  cut into equal-sized pieces
1 tablespoon olive oil
½ teaspoon Garam Masala Blend (see recipe page 253)
kosher salt and freshly ground pepper to taste

Lentils

1 tablespoon canola oil or olive oil
3 cardamom pods
1–3 dried hot peppers, e.g., Thai chilis
½ sweet onion, minced
1 carrot, diced
2 garlic cloves, minced
1½ cups vegetable broth
½ cup dried green or beluga lentils, rinsed
1 orange, zest
1 teaspoon Garam Masala Blend (see recipe page 253)
½ teaspoon kosher salt

Garnish:

orange zest
fresh chopped dill
½ cup unsalted peanuts, chopped

Method:

1. Beets: Preheat oven to 400°. Line a baking pan with parchment paper.

2. In a medium bowl, mix the beets with the olive oil, Garam Masala Blend, salt and pepper. Evenly spread on the baking pan, making sure not to overcrowd, and roast in the oven for 20–25 minutes until soft on the inside and crispy on the outside. Keep warm and set aside.

3. Lentils: While beets are roasting, prepare the lentils. In a large cast iron skillet over medium heat, warm the oil until hot and shimmery. Add cardamom pods and dried peppers and cook, stirring frequently until fragrant, about 1 minute.

4. Add onions and sauté until lightly browned, about 1–2 minutes. Then add carrots and garlic and stir frequently until the garlic is fragrant, about 1–2 minutes. Mix in broth, lentils, orange zest, Garam Masala Blend and salt. Bring to a boil and then reduce heat to medium-low and simmer. Stir occasionally until lentils are cooked, about 20 minutes. Remove cardamom pods and peppers.

5. Serve using a slotted spoon to reduce the liquid. Place the lentils on the plate and top with the roasted beets.

6. Garnish with orange zest, dill and chopped peanuts.

Helpful Tips:

If dried hot peppers are not available, substitute with ½ teaspoon dried red pepper flakes.

BEETS
WITH
LIME
AND
PANELA
CHEESE

Serves 4

Beets originated from the Mediterranean and were brought to the Americas by European colonizers. There are many varieties that are used for human consumption, sugar and animal feed production. Roughly one-third of the world's sugar comes from sugar beets.

Ingredients:

1 pound red beets, unpeeled, washed and cut into equal-sized pieces

2 tablespoons canola oil

1 tablespoon Southwest Spice Blend (see recipe page 254)

½ teaspoon dried oregano

¼ teaspoon kosher salt

Garnish:

¼ cup crumbled panela cheese

1 lime, cut into wedges

Pickled Red Onions (see recipe page 204)

Method:

1. Preheat the oven to 400° and line a baking pan with parchment paper.

2. In a large bowl, mix beets and canola oil. Add seasonings and toss well. Spread seasoned beets evenly on the baking pan, making sure not to overcrowd them.

3. Roast in the oven for 20–25 minutes. Remove when the beets are crisp on the outside and tender on the inside.

4. Top with cheese crumbles, lime wedges and pickled onions before serving.

Helpful Tips:

Substitute any root vegetable for beets. Adjust cooking time if needed.

Substitute with queso fresco or cotija cheese if panela cheese is not available at your local grocery store.

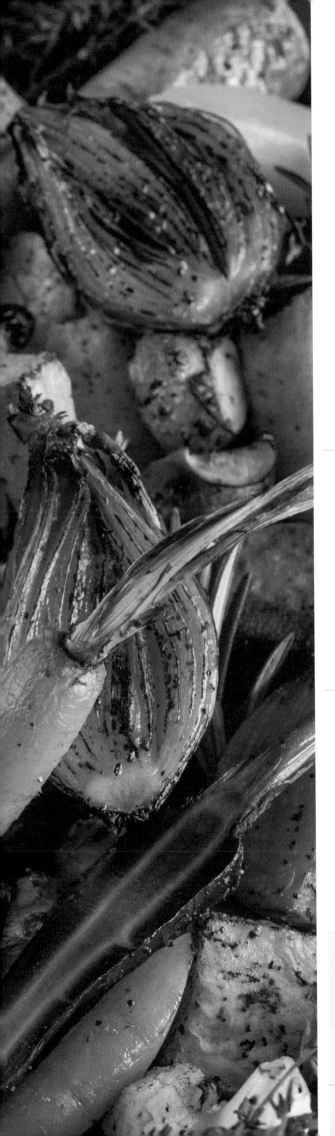

ROASTED WINTER VEGETABLES

Serves 4

Winter root vegetables such as beets, turnips and carrots are often knobby, bulbous and shaggy. But don't let their appearance discourage you because they are often the most flavorful offering of the produce section. Look for winter roots to be firm and heavy with no signs of sprouting or shriveling. These crops are all cool-season vegetables that are best planted in the early fall or early spring. They will develop with edible leafy green tops showing above ground, while the bulk of the vegetable, also edible, grows underground as a root. Sometimes these root vegetables will have small branching side roots that help the plant gather more water and oxygen from the surrounding soil. Once harvested, the entire vegetable can be eaten — even the skin — but just give it a good scrub in cold water before cooking.

Ingredients:

1 pound of assorted winter vegetables
  (beets, turnips and carrots)
2 tablespoons canola oil
1 teaspoon dried oregano
2 sprigs of rosemary
3 sprigs of thyme
1 teaspoon unsalted chili powder
½ teaspoon kosher salt
½ teaspoon freshly ground black pepper

Method:

1. Preheat the oven to 400° and line a baking pan with parchment paper.

2. Cut vegetables into equal-sized pieces and place in a large mixing bowl.

3. Add oil and seasonings. Mix well. Spread on the pan, making sure not to overcrowd the vegetables.

4. Roast in the oven for 25–30 minutes or until crisp on the outside and tender on the inside.

Helpful Tips:

Wash, don't peel, your vegetables.

Roasting time varies based on the size of the vegetable cuts.

The ratio of seasoning is 1 pound of vegetables to 2 tablespoons of oil and 1 tablespoon of seasoning.

**HOW
GOOD
FOOD
WORKS
IN THE
KITCHEN**

Bulbs, Tubers and Rhizomes

Herb and Garlic Spread, Pickled Red Onions, Roasted Garlic, Sweet Onion Dip

HERB AND GARLIC SPREAD

Yields about 1 cup

Garlic is used around the world in many different cultures and preparations, usually as a background player. This herb and garlic spread brings the bulb to the forefront to showcase its distinctive, sharp flavor. The strong smell and taste of garlic comes from the compound allicin, which is released in greater quantities the more the garlic breaks down; finely minced garlic has a stronger fragrance than whole, intact cloves. At the supermarket, choose plump and firm garlic bulbs with tight, papery skin — or you can plant a clove, with its skin still on and pointed tip up, in a pot with drainage holes to grow your own. Your home-grown garlic will be ready to harvest in about eight months when the green shoots begin to wilt and fall over.

Ingredients:

2 garlic cloves, peeled and finely grated

¾ cup low-fat mayonnaise

¼ cup fat-free Greek yogurt, strained

2 tablespoons olive oil

¼ teaspoon kosher salt

2 tablespoons finely chopped fresh oregano

1 tablespoon finely chopped fresh dill, stems removed

1 tablespoon finely chopped fresh mint, stems removed

Method:

1. In a blender or food processor, combine grated garlic, mayonnaise, yogurt, olive oil and salt. Blend until smooth. Fold in fresh herbs. Store in an airtight container in the refrigerator for up to 1 week.

Helpful Tips:

This spread is highly versatile, working well in many different dishes. Try using it as a topping for baked fish or as an appetizer served with crackers. It's also delicious on a bagel or sandwich with sliced turkey or ham.

PICKLED RED ONIONS

Serves 4

Red onions, like garlic or other onion varieties, are fairly easy to grow in a home garden. Choose a site in full sunlight and plant seeds or transplants in late fall or early winter. When the sprouts are about 6 inches tall, thin the rows to one plant every 2–3 inches — this gives the bulbs plenty of room to develop and grow. Onion bulbs should be ready for harvest in May or June, when the green stem begins to weaken and fall over. Remove the onion bulb from the soil and leave outside to dry. After two days, bring your home-grown onions inside to enjoy raw, sautéed, roasted or pickled. The vibrant red and purple color of red onions makes them the perfect variety to pickle and to add to sandwiches, pizzas or tacos.

Ingredients:

1 red onion, thinly sliced

¾ cup white vinegar

¼ cup water

1 tablespoon honey

½ teaspoon kosher salt

¼ teaspoon red pepper flakes

Method:

1. Add sliced onions to a sterilized 12-ounce jar.

2. In a small saucepan, add vinegar, water, honey, salt and red pepper flakes and bring the mixture to a boil. Remove from the heat and pour the vinegar mixture over the onions, leaving about a ½ inch of space at the top of the jar. Secure the lid on the jar and allow it to seal by cooling. Once cool, store in the refrigerator for up to 1 week.

Helpful Tips:

We recommend using a glass or ceramic container to store pickled vegetables. Metal will react with the vinegar, and plastics will absorb the flavor.

ROASTED GARLIC

Yields 2 garlic heads

While garlic is used around the world, its true "center of origin" is Central Asia, the only area where wild garlic grows without human assistance. Garlic has a long history as one of the world's oldest crops, cultivated in ancient China, India, Egypt and Greece for its purported medicinal properties. It was thought that garlic could treat infections, plagues and parasites and increase the vitality and capability of soldiers and slaves. Garlic was even consumed by athletes at the first Olympic Games as the original performance enhancer. Now garlic is recognized as having antimicrobial and antioxidant properties, and in conjunction with a balanced diet, may protect against cancer and heart disease.

Ingredients:

2 garlic heads
¼ cup olive oil
3–4 fresh thyme sprigs
2–3 fresh rosemary sprigs

Method:

1. Preheat the oven to 400° and line a loaf pan with foil.

2. Remove the outer loose layers of skin from garlic heads and cut off the tops to expose the cloves inside. Place the garlic heads cut side up in the pan. Place the thyme and rosemary sprigs on top. Drizzle with olive oil.

3. Cover the pan tightly with foil. Transfer to the oven and roast for 40–45 minutes or until garlic is tender and caramelized.

Helpful Tips:

Use muffin tins to roast multiple garlic heads at once.

Our Roasted Garlic makes a great appetizer served with crackers, or squeeze out the garlic to use in mashed potatoes, sauces, stews or soups.

Roasted garlic can stay in the refrigerator for two weeks if stored in an airtight container with a small amount of olive oil on top. It can also be frozen for one month in the freezer.

SWEET ONION DIP

Serves 6

Have you ever wondered why cooked onions have a less sharp, sweeter and more complex flavor? You can thank the Maillard reaction for that. The Maillard reaction occurs between amino acids and sugars when heat is added, creating browning and depth of flavor. Heat also breaks down sugar molecules from the larger sucrose to the smaller glucose and fructose, contributing to the sweetness of cooked onions. When combined with silken tofu and vinegar, the golden-brown onions create a delicious dip.

Ingredients:

1 tablespoon canola oil
2 sweet onions, cut in half and sliced evenly
½ teaspoon kosher salt
1 cup silken tofu
1 teaspoon white vinegar
¼ cup minced fresh chives
1 tablespoon pine nuts, toasted

Method:

1. In a 10-inch cast iron pan over medium heat, warm the oil until hot and shimmery. Add onions and salt and sauté until softened. Turn heat down to medium-low and cook for 30–40 minutes, stirring frequently. If pan becomes dry, add a little water and turn heat to low. Onions will be done when they are a golden brown color.

2. In a blender or food processor, combine onions, silken tofu and vinegar. Blend until smooth. Fold in chives. Store in an airtight container in the refrigerator. When ready to serve, top with pine nuts.

Helpful Tips:

Onions can be prepared ahead of time and refrigerated for 3–4 days or frozen.

Substitute ½ cup Greek yogurt and ½ cup sour cream for tofu if desired.

Serve with crackers, whole grain bagel chips or fresh vegetables as an appetizer.

LEEK, MUSHROOM AND SAUSAGE SOUP

Serves 6

Like onions and garlic, leeks belong to the Allium family and grow underground with tall green leaves extending from the ground. But unlike onions and garlic, the edible portion of a leek is a cylindrical stalk shape rather than a bulb. Because leeks have dirt piled up around them as they grow to create a longer stalk, they must be thoroughly cleaned before cooking. Trim off the dark green portions of the leaves and cut the leek lengthwise starting at the leaves and moving two-thirds down the stalk. Spread apart the layers and rinse under cool, running water. The mild and sweet onion-like taste of leeks helps enhance the rich and savory flavors of this Italian-inspired soup.

Ingredients:

1 tablespoon olive oil

2 leeks, cleaned, dark leaves removed,
   white part thinly sliced

8 ounces beech mushrooms or any other savory variety

2 garlic cloves, minced

8 ounces chicken sausage, casings removed

¼ cup red wine

1 bay leaf

1 tablespoon Italian seasoning

1 teaspoon sweet paprika

½ teaspoon kosher salt

½ cup whole wheat orzo pasta

1 cup water

1 cup crushed tomatoes

2 cups Vegetable Broth (see recipe page 264)

½ cup sour cream

2 tablespoons minced fresh parsley, stems removed

1 zucchini, thinly sliced into "noodles"
   using a vegetable spiralizer

Method:

1. In a large soup pot, warm oil until hot and shimmery. Add leeks and sauté until golden brown, about 3–4 minutes. Add mushrooms and garlic and cook until mushrooms release their water and are browned, about 3–5 minutes. Add chicken sausage and break it up with a spoon. Cook until browned, about 3–5 minutes.

2. Add red wine and deglaze the pot by stirring to loosen the browned bits in the bottom. Stir in bay leaf, Italian seasoning, paprika, salt, orzo pasta, water, crushed tomatoes and broth. Bring mixture to a boil, reduce heat and simmer uncovered until orzo pasta is tender, about 10–12 minutes.

3. Garnish each soup bowl with a dollop of sour cream, parsley and zucchini noodles.

Helpful Tips:

Zucchini "noodles" are sometimes available in the produce section of the grocery store.

JICAMA, MANGO AND SCALLOP SOUTHWEST SALAD

Serves 4

The tuber jicama is popular in Mexico, Central and South America and Southeast Asia but may be unfamiliar to most Americans. It has a very light sweet, nutty and crisp flavor, like a savory apple, and adds a great crunch to salads, spring rolls or stir fries. To prepare shredded jicama, begin by cleaning it well, then trimming away the brown exterior. Because the skin is so tough, it is best to use a chef's knife rather than a vegetable peeler. Trim the top and bottom of the jicama to create a flat place for it to lie, then slide the knife under the skin, working from top to bottom. After peeling, cut the jicama into quarters and run over a grater to shred. The light and neutral flavor of jicama makes it the perfect addition to this tangy and spicy Southwest salad with scallops.

Ingredients:

Dressing:

¼ cup olive oil

¼ cup fresh lime juice (about 2 limes)

1 tablespoon honey

1 teaspoon lime zest

1 teaspoon Southwest Spice Blend
   (see recipe page 254)

½ teaspoon cumin

Salad:

2–3 bunches romaine lettuce, core removed,
   chopped (about 3 cups)

½ jicama, shredded (about 1 cup)

1 can low-sodium black beans (15 ounces),
   drained and rinsed

2 ears of corn, kernels removed (about 1 cup)

1 avocado, diced

1 mango, diced

½ cup unsalted pumpkin seeds, roasted

¼ cup thinly sliced green onions

Scallops:

12 ounces scallops, side muscle removed and
   patted dry with a paper towel

1 teaspoon Southwest Spice Blend
   (see recipe page 254)

1 tablespoon olive oil

½ lime, juiced

1 tablespoon unsalted butter

Method:

1. Dressing: In a 12-ounce mason jar or similar container, combine olive oil, lime juice, honey, lime zest, Southwest Spice Blend and cumin. Secure the lid and shake until fully mixed. Set aside.

2. Salad: In a large serving bowl, combine romaine lettuce and jicama and toss with half of the salad dressing. Top the lettuce mixture with even sections of black beans, corn, avocado and mango.

3. Seared scallops: Season scallops with Southwest Spice Blend. In a large sauté pan over medium-high heat, warm oil until hot and shimmery. Add scallops and cook until golden brown, about 1–2 minutes. Using tongs, gently turn the scallops and cook for another 1-2 minutes. Remove the scallops and keep warm. Add the lime juice to deglaze the pan using a spoon to release the fond. Add the butter and stir to incorporate. Add the scallops back to the pan and gently toss in the sauce. Place the scallops on top of the salad and drizzle with the remaining dressing.

4. Garnish: Top with pumpkin seeds and green onions.

Helpful Tips:

The easiest way to cut a mango is the same as the jicama. Slice off the top of both ends so it sits solidly on the counter and then cut slices around the pit.

POTATO CRUSTED SHEPHERD'S PIE

Serves 6

The hearty potato is almost as easy to grow as it is to cook. Instead of growing from seeds like other vegetables, pieces of mature potatoes known as "seed potatoes" are used to produce a crop of the starchy tubers. The eyes, or small dimples, of a potato are what sprout into new plants — you may have seen this happen if you've ever left a potato in the pantry for too long. After obtaining seed potatoes from a reputable source, store them in a warm, damp spot for two weeks before planting to allow sprouts to begin developing. For a fall crop, plant potatoes in August. Choose a site in full sun, and plant the seed potatoes 3 inches deep. As the plant grows, continue pulling dirt in toward the plant to create a small mound. This ensures the potatoes have ample space to grow and protects them from sunlight, which causes green patches on the skin. Your potatoes will be ready to harvest when the above-ground plant begins to die. Take care not to puncture the tubers as you dig them up from the ground and make sure to scrub them clean before cooking.

Ingredients:

Potatoes:

3 Yukon Gold potatoes (about 1 pound), diced

½ cauliflower head (about ½ pound),
   florets only, chopped

2 tablespoons unsalted butter

2 tablespoons Greek yogurt

½ teaspoon kosher salt

¼ teaspoon freshly ground black pepper

1 egg yolk

¼ cup whole milk, if needed

Filling:

1 tablespoon canola oil

½ onion, diced

2 carrots, diced

½ cup finely chopped button mushrooms

3 garlic cloves, minced

1 pound ground lamb, lean (80/20)

2 teaspoons Worcestershire sauce

2 tablespoons all-purpose flour

½ cup cooked lentils

¾ cup frozen peas

¾ cup frozen corn

1 cup vegetable broth

1 teaspoon dried parsley

1 teaspoon dried thyme

1 teaspoon dried rosemary

½ teaspoon kosher salt

½ teaspoon freshly ground black pepper

¼ cup thinly sliced green onions

Method:

1. Potatoes: Place potatoes and cauliflower in a large pot and cover with water. Bring the pot to a boil over medium-high heat and then reduce the heat to a simmer. Simmer until potatoes and cauliflower are tender but not mushy, about 10 minutes. Remove from the heat and strain, taking extra care to remove all the excess water. Transfer cooked cauliflower and potatoes to a bowl and use a potato masher or a hand electric mixer to blend well. Add butter, Greek yogurt, salt, pepper and egg yolk and mix until smooth, only adding milk if needed to thin out the mash consistency. Set aside.

2. Filling: While the potatoes are cooking, preheat the oven to 375°. In a large cast iron pan or oven-ready pan over medium heat, warm oil until hot and shimmery. Add onion and carrots and sauté until lightly browned, about 5 minutes. Add mushrooms and garlic and cook until mushrooms release their water and are browned, about 3–5 minutes. Add ground lamb and cook until browned, about 7–10 minutes. Stir in Worcestershire sauce. Sprinkle flour over mixture and stir to combine. Add lentils, peas, corn, vegetable broth, herbs, salt and pepper and stir to combine. Bring mixture to a boil, reduce heat and simmer. Cook, stirring occasionally, until mixture is slightly thickened, about 5–8 minutes. Remove from the heat.

3. Assemble: Add the mashed potato mixture to the top of the lamb and lentils in the pan, making sure to spread it evenly across the top to create a seal. Bake uncovered for 25 minutes or until the top is golden brown. Garnish with green onions.

FINGERLING POTATOES, RAINBOW CARROTS
AND
TROUT FILLETS

Serves 4

Unlike new potatoes, which are harvested before they are fully grown, the cultivation of fingerling potatoes results in small, narrow tubers at full maturity. As the name suggests, fingerling potatoes resemble fingers and can have tan, red or purple exteriors. The skin is much thinner than that of their larger counterparts, and they spoil quicker. So make sure to use them before they begin to sprout, which is within about two weeks of purchase. The interior of a fingerling has a creamy, waxy texture and is lower in starch than a variety like a russet. The lower starch content of the fingerling means it will hold its shape better when roasted, making it the perfect variety for this delicious, herb and citrusy one-pan potato, carrot and trout recipe.

Ingredients:

3 tablespoons olive oil, divided use

½ pound baby rainbow carrots (greens reserved), cut lengthwise

½ pound fingerling potatoes, unpeeled and halved

4 trout fillets, skin on (about 1 pound)

1 teaspoon dried oregano

½ teaspoon kosher salt

¼ teaspoon freshly ground black pepper

4 garlic cloves, thinly sliced lengthwise

1 lemon, halved, seeds removed

Carrot Top Pesto (see recipe page 256)

Method:

1. Preheat the oven to 400°. Brush 1 tablespoon oil evenly on a baking pan and place in the oven for 10 minutes so the pan gets very hot.

2. Remove pan and carefully spread carrots and potatoes, making room for the trout fillets, which should be placed skin-side down. Drizzle vegetables and trout with 2 tablespoons oil and season with oregano, salt and pepper.

3. Spread garlic slices evenly over the mixture and add lemon halves cut side down to the pan.

4. Roast in the oven until trout reaches an internal temperature of 135° and remove from the pan, about 8 minutes. Set the fish aside and keep warm. Leave the carrots and potatoes in the oven until they are crisp on the outside and tender on the inside, about 10–15 additional minutes. Remove from the oven and squeeze lemon juice over the fish and vegetables.

5. Serve with Carrot Top Pesto.

Helpful Tips:

Trout, a freshwater fish, is a member of the salmon family. There are various types, but rainbow trout is the one you should be on the hunt for.

Trout, like salmon, contains pin bones that need to be removed prior to eating.

ROASTED POTATOES AND CARROTS WITH TRUFFLE OIL

Serves 4

Potatoes had to make a few trips across the Atlantic before they were introduced into North American cuisine. The starchy tubers were first cultivated in the South American Andes roughly 8,000 years ago and were brought back to Europe in the 1500s by Spanish conquistadors. It took almost a century for potatoes to gain popularity in Europe, and in the 1600s, potatoes were introduced to North America by European colonizers. Today, many colors, shapes and varieties of potatoes populate grocery stores, restaurants and home kitchens. One variety, the fingerling, has a rich, nutty and buttery taste that is the perfect vessel for umami seasoning and truffle oil in this crispy and colorful recipe.

Ingredients:

½ pound fingerling potatoes, halved

½ pound carrots, cut into equal-sized pieces

2 tablespoons olive oil

3 garlic cloves, minced

2 tablespoons minced fresh thyme, stems removed

1 teaspoon Umami Spice Blend (see recipe page 253)

1 tablespoon white truffle oil

½ teaspoon kosher salt

Method:

1. Preheat the oven to 400° and line a baking pan with parchment paper.

2. In a large bowl, add potatoes and carrots. Pour olive oil over the vegetables. Combine with garlic, thyme and umami seasoning. Spread seasoned vegetables evenly on the baking sheet, making sure not to overcrowd.

3. Roast in the oven for 25–30 minutes until they are crisp on the outside and tender on the inside.

4. Remove from the oven, drizzle with truffle oil and season with salt before serving.

Helpful Tips:

Substitute 1 tablespoon of dried thyme for fresh thyme. We used an heirloom Parisian baby carrot in our picture, but any carrot would work well in this recipe.

HOW
GOOD
FOOD
WORKS
IN THE
KITCHEN

Stems and Shoots

SAUTÉED FIDDLEHEAD FERNS
AND
LEEKS

Serves 4

Fiddlehead ferns are the tightly coiled ends of the ostrich fern leaves and look like small spirals gently emerging from the soil during April and May. Fiddleheads have a mild, nutty flavor and have been described as tasting like a mixture of asparagus and spinach. While most fiddleheads are collected through foraging, it is recommended that individuals collect them with an experienced guide as many varieties of ferns can look similar. Although they are not widely available, some specialty grocery stores and farmers markets carry the tender spring spirals.

Ingredients:

1 pound fiddlehead ferns, trimmed and cleaned

1 tablespoon olive oil

1 small leek (white and light green portions),
   washed and thinly sliced

1 tablespoon freshly grated horseradish or
   substitute prepared horseradish

2 garlic cloves, minced

2 tablespoons chopped fresh parsley, stems removed

1 tablespoon capers, rinsed

¼ teaspoon kosher salt

¼ teaspoon freshly ground black pepper

2 tablespoons dry white wine

1 tablespoon unsalted butter

Method:

1. Blanch and shock: Create an ice bath by placing ice in a large bowl and covering with water. Set aside. In a medium-sized pot, bring 2 quarts of water to a boil. Add fiddleheads and cook for 1–2 minutes. Transfer fiddleheads to the ice bath and let cool for about a minute. Remove to a layer of paper towels to let dry.

2. Sautéed leeks and fiddleheads: In a large skillet over medium heat, warm oil until hot and shimmery. Add leeks and sauté until tender and fragrant, about 2–3 minutes. Add blanched fiddleheads and sauté until golden brown, about 2–3 minutes. Add horseradish, garlic, parsley, capers, salt and pepper and sauté until fragrant, about 1–2 minutes. Stir in white wine to deglaze the pan and continue cooking until the liquid is reduced by half. Remove from the heat and stir in butter.

Helpful Tips:

The white and light green portions of leeks are mellow in flavor, while the dark green portion is tougher and imparts a stronger flavor to dishes. Since this recipe is quick cooking, we suggest only using the white and light green portions.

To wash leeks, place the trimmed portion in a bowl of water to allow any sand and dirt to fall to the bottom. Scoop out the leeks, leaving the dirt and sand in the bowl.

Celery Spring Rolls with Peanut Sauce

CELERY SPRING ROLLS WITH PEANUT SAUCE

Yields 8 spring rolls

Chinese celery has a bolder flavor and is much thinner than the traditional celery found at the grocery store. It has an abundance of leaves that resemble Italian parsley. Growing Chinese celery isn't difficult, but it's best to start with a seed planted in trays. Once growth has started, transplant to the garden. It needs full sun and should be planted when the risk of frost has passed. Chinese celery is rarely eaten raw since its intense flavor can overpower other spices. Store your celery in the crisper drawer in the refrigerator and don't fret if it becomes limp after a few days — this is common and can be easily reversed with a quick soak in ice water.

Ingredients:

Peanut sauce:
½ cup smooth peanut butter

2 tablespoons lime juice

2 tablespoons low-sodium soy sauce

2 tablespoons honey

1 tablespoon freshly grated ginger (about 1-inch piece)

1½ teaspoons lemongrass chili paste or chili paste

2 tablespoons water, as needed

Spring rolls:
8 spring-roll rice papers

¼ cup fresh cilantro leaves, torn

¼ cup fresh mint leaves, torn

¼ cup fresh basil leaves, torn

½ cup Chinese celery leaves, torn

4–6 stalks of Chinese celery,
  thinly sliced, leaves reserved for garnish

1 cucumber, thinly sliced

¼ head of purple cabbage, thinly sliced

1 carrot, thinly sliced

1 red bell pepper, thinly sliced

½ cup unsalted peanuts, roasted and chopped

Method:

1. Peanut sauce: In a small bowl, add all sauce ingredients, except water, and whisk until smooth. Add water as needed for consistency. Set aside.

2. Spring rolls: Arrange a mixture of cilantro, mint, basil and celery leaves on each wrapper. Add a portion of celery stalk, cucumbers, cabbage, carrots and bell peppers on the lower third of the wrapper, leaving about 1-inch of space on the sides. Fold the bottom of the wrapper over the veggies, then fold the uncovered sides inward and roll up the wrapper as tightly as possible. Repeat with remaining ingredients. Serve with a portion of peanut sauce.

Helpful Tips:

This recipe can be adapted to add additional protein like sliced tofu, chicken or beef.

Use a variety of vegetables — just make sure they are similar in size.

LEMONGRASS, BELL PEPPER
AND
TOFU

Serves 4

Native to India, lemongrass is used extensively in Southeast Asian cooking. It has a floral, lemon flavor with hints of ginger. When selecting lemongrass at the grocery store, choose firm stalks with very pale, yellow lower portions and vibrant green tops. Store it in the refrigerator wrapped in a damp paper towel. Large pieces of lemongrass stalk are often too fibrous to eat and should be removed from the dish before serving.

Ingredients:

2 tablespoons cornstarch

8 ounces tofu, extra firm and pressed between
  paper towels to dry and cut into cubes

3 tablespoons avocado oil, divided use

½ head of cauliflower, cut into equal-sized florets

½ head of broccoli, cut into equal-sized florets

½-inch piece of fresh ginger root,
  peeled and grated

2 garlic cloves, thinly sliced

3 lemongrass stalks, roots trimmed,
  cut into 4-inch pieces (see tip below)

2 Thai chili peppers

3 bell peppers, assorted colors, thinly sliced

½ cup vegetable broth or water

1 teaspoon fish sauce

½ cup canned coconut milk, shaken well

½ cup unsalted peanuts, toasted

1 lime, juiced

kosher salt to taste

2 cups steamed brown rice

¼ bunch green onions, thinly sliced

1 cup fresh basil leaves, cut lengthwise

Method:

1. In a zip lock bag, add cornstarch and tofu. Seal and gently shake tofu until all pieces are covered. Open bag and add tofu to colander and shake off excess cornstarch. Set aside.

2. In a large sauté pan over medium-high heat, warm 1 tablespoon oil until hot and shimmery. Add tofu in one layer and let brown, then continue turning each piece until all sides of the cubes are browned. Remove from the pan and set aside.

3. In the pan, add 2 tablespoons of oil and add cauliflower and broccoli and sauté until brown about 6-8 minutes. Add ginger, garlic, lemongrass and peppers and stir fry quickly to prevent the seasoning and spices from burning, but allowing them to become fragrant. Add vegetable broth or water, fish sauce and coconut milk and bring to a boil. Reduce heat to a simmer and continue cooking until vegetables are tender and liquid is reduced, about 8-10 minutes. Add tofu back to the pan and warm together. Stir in peanuts, lime juice and salt.

4. When ready, remove lemongrass stalks. Plate over a portion of brown rice and garnish with green onions and freshly chopped basil.

Helpful Tips:

In order to release the flavor of the lemongrass stalks, they should be pounded with a meat mallet or rolling pin before being cut into smaller pieces.

Tofu is a great protein to marinate. The curds are loosely coagulated, so flavor is able to move toward the center of the block, adding tremendous flavor. Also, cubed tofu allows more contact with the marinade, adding additional flavor.

Swiss Chard, Shrimp and Grits

SWISS CHARD, SHRIMP AND GRITS

Serves 4

Swiss chard is known for its big, bright-green leaves and rainbow-colored stems that add pink, yellow and orange hues to garden beds. It can be grown in cool or warm climates, making it convenient to use year round in recipes for a touch of color and to add nutrients to a variety of dishes. It's known as the "leafy beet," as the plants are closely related and both are entirely edible.

Shrimp and grits is usually considered a Southern dish, but its roots are from Africa, where maize was ground into a texture like today's grits and combined with shellfish.

Ingredients:

Grits:

3 cups water

½ teaspoon kosher salt

1½ cups stone-ground corn grits

4 tablespoons unsalted butter, cut into pieces

1 cup shredded cheddar cheese

Chard and shrimp:

12 ounces shrimp, peeled, deveined and
   patted dry with a paper towel

2 teaspoons dried oregano

1 teaspoon chili powder

2 tablespoons canola oil

1 cup cherry tomatoes

½ onion, finely minced

1 bunch Swiss chard, leaves roughly chopped and
   stems finely diced

4 garlic cloves, minced

1 teaspoon smoked paprika

1 lemon, zest and juice, separated

½ teaspoon kosher salt

Method:

1. Grits: In a large pot over high heat, add water and salt and bring to a boil. Reduce heat to a simmer and whisk in grits. Cook for 5 minutes, stirring occasionally. Remove from the heat and stir in butter and cheese. Set aside and keep warm.

2. Chard and shrimp: Season shrimp with oregano and chili powder. Heat oil in a cast iron pan and sauté shrimp until pink, about 2–3 minutes on each side. Remove from the pan and set aside. Add tomatoes and allow to char, about 4–5 minutes. Add onions and chard stems, and sauté until lightly browned, about 2–3 minutes. Add garlic and smoked paprika. Continue cooking until the garlic is fragrant, about 1–2 minutes. Stir in the chard leaves, lemon juice and lemon zest. Continue cooking until the chard is wilted, about 3–4 minutes. Add the shrimp back in to the pan and toss to coat. Season with salt as desired.

3. To serve: Plate a spoonful of grits and top with chard and shrimp.

Helpful Tips:

When the dish is ready to be plated, you might use a slotted spoon to drain off some of the liquid produced from the cooked tomatoes.

Asparagus, Spinach and Mushroom Quiche

ASPARAGUS, SPINACH AND MUSHROOM QUICHE

Serves 6

Asparagus stem thickness varies depending on the age of the plant. Older plants have thick stems, while young plants have thin stems. So the difference comes not from watering habits or varying soils but age. Make sure to select asparagus that has the buds still tight against the stem and opt for thicker asparagus when using high-heat cooking methods like broiling, grilling or pan-searing. The higher water content will prevent the spears from drying out.

Ingredients:

Crust:

¾ cup whole rolled oats

½ cup all-purpose flour

¼ cup almond flour

⅓ cup Parmesan cheese, grated

pinch of kosher salt

3 tablespoons unsalted butter, cold, cut into small pieces

¼ cup buttermilk, cold

Vegetable filling:

1 tablespoon olive oil

2 leeks, white and light green parts, diced

½ cup button mushrooms, thinly sliced

1 garlic clove, minced

1 cup baby spinach leaves, packed

8–10 asparagus spears, ends trimmed, 4 spears cut in half lengthwise 4 spears cut into 1-inch pieces

½ teaspoon dried thyme

½ teaspoon kosher salt

Quiche:

4 eggs

2 egg whites

1 cup 2% milk

½ teaspoon kosher salt

¼ teaspoon freshly ground black pepper

⅔ cup shredded Gruyere cheese

Method:

1. Crust: Preheat the oven to 400° and spray a 10-inch tart pan with cooking spray. In a food processor, add rolled oats, all-purpose and almond flour, Parmesan cheese and salt and pulse a few times to combine the mixture. Add butter and pulse until the mixture resembles a coarse meal (pebbly texture). Add buttermilk and continue pulsing until combined. Remove from the food processor and form into a dough ball. Place the dough between two pieces of wax paper. Using a rolling pin, form the dough into an 11-inch circle. Remove one side of the wax paper and flip the dough into the pie dish and press it into the form of the dish. Remove the top sheet of wax paper. Transfer to the oven and bake for 8–9 minutes. Remove and let cool. Reduce the oven to 350°.

2. Vegetable filling: In a large cast iron pan over medium heat, warm oil until hot and shimmery. Add leeks and sauté until translucent, about 1–2 minutes. Add mushrooms and garlic and cook until the mushrooms release their water and are browned, about 3–5 minutes. The water should be evaporated. Add spinach, small asparagus pieces, thyme and salt and cook until the spinach is wilted and the liquid is reduced, about 3–5 minutes. Remove from the heat and let cool.

3. Quiche: In a large bowl, whisk together eggs and egg whites until combined. Pour in milk and continue to whisk. Add salt and pepper. Spread cheese over the crust, add the spinach, asparagus and mushroom mixture and pour the egg mixture on top. Place the asparagus halves on top for decoration. Bake for 45–50 minutes or until a toothpick inserted into the center comes out clean.

Helpful Tips:

It's best to let the quiche rest until slightly cooled so it sets properly before slicing.

This recipe also works well with a 9-inch pie pan.

ASPARAGUS
AND
SALMON
EN PAPILLOTE

Serves 4

Asparagus has a remarkable history that dates back to wall drawings by the ancient Egyptians 3,000 years ago. Cultivation began with the Greeks and Romans, who ate it fresh in the spring and dried it for food in the winter. It was brought to North America by European settlers in the 1600s and was considered a delicacy by French royalty when Madame de Pompadour referred to it as "points d'amour," or love points. In this recipe, asparagus is thinly sliced and packaged with salmon inside a parchment pouch, a French cooking method called *en papillote*. This method allows the asparagus and salmon to gently steam in the oven, creating a tender and juicy final dish.

Ingredients:

4 parchment paper pieces,
   each cut into 15x17-inch rectangles
½ bunch of asparagus (about 8 ounces),
   ends trimmed and thinly sliced on the bias
1 small leek, white and light green parts only,
   thinly sliced, washed well and drained
4 teaspoons olive oil
kosher salt and freshly ground black pepper to taste
4 skinless salmon fillets
   (about 4 ounces each and 1-inch thick)
4 tablespoons white wine or vegetable broth
¼ cup packed fresh herbs
   (tarragon, dill, basil, parsley or a combination)
2 lemons (1 lemon thinly sliced and 1 lemon
   cut into wedges)
4 teaspoons unsalted butter

Method:

1. Preheat oven to 400°. Fold each parchment piece in half crosswise to make a crease then unfold and lay flat.

2. In a bowl, toss asparagus and leeks with oil. Season with salt and pepper.

3. Brush 1 teaspoon of olive oil over each fillet and season with salt and pepper. Arrange a fillet to one side of the crease on each parchment piece. Pour 1 tablespoon of white wine over each fish fillet then top with the asparagus mixture and lemon slices, dividing them evenly. Add 1 teaspoon butter on top of each fillet. Fold parchment paper around the edges tightly in ¼-inch folds to create a half-moon shape and make sure to press the crimps and folds firmly to seal the packets well so steam will not escape.

4. Bake on a rimmed baking sheet, 12 minutes for medium-rare. You won't be able to tell the temperature of the salmon until you open the parchment packets, so time is a good measure, but medium-rare salmon should be 120° and medium 125°. Transfer to plates and carefully cut packets open to release the steam. Top with herbs, squeeze over lemon juice and serve.

Helpful Tips:

If you are in a hurry, this cooking technique can be done in the microwave since the salmon is cooked by steaming.

The dish can also be made in one large parchment packet to serve family style.

Salmon will cook quickly, so it is important to have thinly sliced vegetables to ensure even cooking.

Asparagus and Garlic Soup

ASPARAGUS
AND
GARLIC
SOUP

Serves 6

Asparagus is a perennial, so once planted, it will return annually for harvest. It takes several seasons before the asparagus is mature enough to harvest, but after those first few years, it will continue to grow in the same place in the garden for 15 to 20 years. The spears can grow in several different colors — green, white or purple. Once harvested, the asparagus should be thoroughly rinsed and can be stored in the refrigerator for up to three days. Make sure to cut off the woody bottoms from the spears to remove any bitterness.

Ingredients:

1 tablespoon olive oil

1 shallot, diced

1 bunch asparagus, ends trimmed, cut into 1½-inch pieces

2 garlic cloves, minced

2 tablespoons minced fresh tarragon, stems removed

1 tablespoon minced fresh dill, stems removed

4 cups vegetable broth

1 can white beans (15 ounces), drained and rinsed

1 tablespoon lemon juice

½ teaspoon kosher salt

Garnish:

1–2 tablespoons olive oil

10–12 asparagus tips

2 tablespoons pickled onion slices

2 tablespoons chopped fresh dill, stems removed

2 tablespoons chopped fresh tarragon, stems removed

Method:

1. In a large soup pot over medium heat, warm oil until hot and shimmery. Add shallots and asparagus and sauté until golden brown, about 3–4 minutes. Remove 10–12 asparagus tips and reserve for garnish. In the pan, add garlic, tarragon and dill and sauté until fragrant, about 1–2 minutes. Stir in broth, beans, lemon juice and salt and bring to a boil. Reduce heat to a simmer until asparagus is tender, about 10–12 minutes.

2. Transfer the mixture in batches to a blender, leave the top vented and blend on high speed until completely smooth.

3. Garnish each soup bowl with a drizzle of olive oil, asparagus tips, pickled onions, dill and tarragon.

Helpful Tips:

Freshly harvested asparagus can be frozen. It should be blanched in boiling water for 1 minute until bright green, removed to a cold water bath, drained, patted dry and placed in an airtight container. The asparagus will keep in the freezer for several months.

ZESTY PICKLED STEMS AND SHOOTS

Humans have been pickling vegetables for more than 4,000 years, since the ancient Mesopotamians began pickling cucumbers. A properly sealed jar of pickled vegetables can safely stay in the pantry for six months and still be delicious. Cucumbers are the most common pickled vegetable, but just about any vegetable (often simply referred to as "pickles") can be treated with water, vinegar, spices and salt to be pickled.

Ingredients:

1½ tablespoons black peppercorns
1½ tablespoons mustard seeds
¼ teaspoon red pepper flakes
2 garlic cloves, peeled and smashed
4–6 celery stalks, washed, peeled
  and trimmed to fit in the jar
4–6 asparagus spears, washed
  and trimmed to fit in the jar
4–6 Swiss chard stems, washed
  and trimmed to fit in the jar
¼ red onion, thinly sliced
1½ cups white vinegar
1½ cups water
2 tablespoons sugar
1½ tablespoons kosher salt

Method:

1. In a sterilized wide-mouth 32-ounce jar, add peppercorns, mustard seeds, red pepper flakes and garlic. Add a mixture of celery stalks, asparagus, Swiss chard stems and onions. Set aside.

2. In a medium-sized pot over medium heat, add vinegar, water, sugar and salt. Bring to a boil while stirring, reduce the heat and cook at a low simmer for about 5 minutes.

3. Remove from the heat and pour the mixture over the vegetables, leaving about ½ inch at the top of the jar. Secure the lid and allow it to seal by cooling.

4. When cool, shake well. Store at room temperature, out of direct sunlight. If the jars were not sterilized, store in the refrigerator.

Helpful Tips:

This recipe can be made as "refrigerator pickles" without heating. Simply add all ingredients to the jar, shake well and store in the refrigerator.

Use a variety of vegetables — just make sure they are similar in size.

FENNEL, BLACKBERRY AND CITRUS SALSA WITH AVOCADO TOAST

Serves 4

Fennel belongs to the Apiaceae family, which also includes carrots, dill, celery and parsley. Fennel has a distinct shape, with a white base, green stalks and feather-like leaves called fronds that are edible and used in culinary dishes. There are two main varieties of fennel: one produces a bulb and the other seeds. Florence fennel is commonly called "bulb fennel," as it is used for the bulb portion of the vegetable; its stalks can grow up to 3 feet in height. Sweet fennel is a taller variety that grows up to 5 feet in height and whose aromatic seeds are used as an herb to enhance recipes.

When purchasing fennel in the grocery store, you will find it has the bulb and fronds attached. In this recipe, we use both.

Ingredients:

Fennel, blackberry and citrus salsa:

½ cup blackberries

1 small fennel bulb, shaved with a mandoline

1 satsuma, peeled and diced

1 Roma tomato, diced

¼ red onion, thinly sliced

1 garlic clove, minced

pinch of kosher salt

Avocado toast:

8 slices whole wheat bread

1 tablespoon olive oil

2 avocados, peeled, pits removed and thinly sliced

1 tablespoon chopped fennel fronds

Method:

1. Fennel, blackberry and citrus salsa: In a medium bowl, combine all ingredients. Refrigerate at least 1 hour before serving.

2. Avocado toast: Preheat the oven to 375° and place bread on a baking pan lined with parchment paper. Brush bread with oil and toast in the oven for 3-5 minutes. Remove and let cool. Top each slice of bread with a layer of avocado, ¼ cup of salsa and garnish with fennel fronds.

Helpful Tips:

If satsuma is not available, substitute with clementine or mandarin oranges.

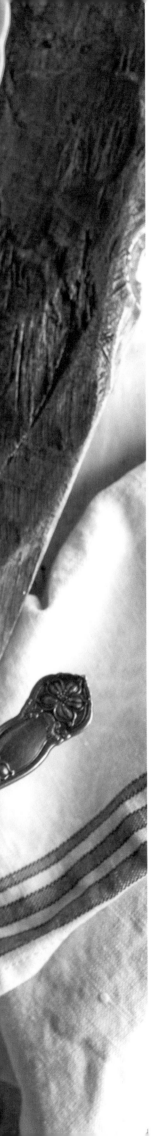

RHUBARB CAKE

Serves 8

Rhubarb is a pink and green perennial vegetable that is commonly used in pies, cakes and jams. The stems, which resemble celery stalks, are the only edible portion of the plant, as the leaves contain oxalic acid, which is poisonous. Rhubarb is harvested when the stalks of the plant are 12 to 18 inches long. One plant might produce rhubarb in the same spot every year for 20 years.

Ingredients:

1 cup all-purpose flour
¼ cup almond flour
1 teaspoon baking powder
½ teaspoon baking soda
½ teaspoon table salt
1 teaspoon ground cardamom
1 cup granulated sugar plus 1 tablespoon for top of the cake
2 eggs, room temperature
½ cup (1 stick) unsalted butter, melted and cooled
½ cup sour cream, room temperature
½ teaspoon almond extract
2 cups rhubarb, trimmed and cut into ½-inch pieces, plus 1 stem sliced into 3 1-inch pieces

Garnish:
½ cup sliced almonds, toasted
1 tablespoon powdered sugar
1 cup whipped cream

Method:

1. Preheat the oven to 350° and spray a 9-inch springform with cooking spray.

2. In a medium-sized bowl, whisk flour, almond flour, baking powder, baking soda, salt and ground cardamom. Set aside. In a large bowl, whisk sugar, eggs and melted butter until combined and well mixed. Add sour cream and almond extract and mix. Continue to whisk and add the flour mixture. Gently fold in rhubarb pieces. Evenly spoon the cake batter into the prepared springform pan. Top it with rhubarb pieces in any desired pattern and sprinkle with 1 tablespoon sugar.

3. Place the springform pan on a large baking pan (in case of a spill). Bake on the middle rack for about 35–45 minutes or until golden brown and a toothpick inserted into the center of the cake comes out clean. If the cake is not set but is browning too soon, loosely cover with foil and return it to the oven to finish.

4. Before serving, garnish the cake with sliced almonds, powdered sugar and whipped cream.

Helpful Tips:
You can use frozen rhubarb, but it must be thawed completely and drained so it does not thin out the batter.

HOW GOOD FOOD WORKS WITH FLAVOR

HOW
GOOD
FOOD
WORKS
WITH
FLAVOR

Spices
Sauces
Pestos
Dressings
Nuts
Oils
Broths

Spices

Spices have added flavor, depth and potential health benefits to foods for most of recorded human history. A spice is any dried part of a plant (other than leaves, which are considered herbs) used to season a dish. Cinnamon is the bark of a tree, paprika comes from ground peppers, cumin is a seed and peppercorn and allspice are dried berries. As the world became more connected, spices were transported from the Middle East to China to Europe to the Americas and back around. Popular spices have their origins in many different cuisines and cultures, and the magic of cooking with spices allows you to bring diversity into your own kitchen, one quarter of a teaspoon at a time. Creating your own spice blends at home not only saves you money but also gives you more freedom and creativity with the ingredients you use.

Umami Spice Blend

Yields ½ cup

Ingredients:

1 ounce dried mushrooms (porcini)
½ teaspoon black peppercorns
½ teaspoon dried thyme
1 teaspoon onion powder
1 teaspoon garlic powder
1 teaspoon nutritional yeast
½ teaspoon ground mustard

Method:

1. Working in batches, add mushrooms, peppercorns and thyme to a spice grinder and pulse until completely milled.

2. Transfer the mixture to an airtight container and add remaining ingredients. Mix well.

3. Store at room temperature, out of direct sunlight.

Helpful Tips:

Use nutritional yeast the same way you would cheese: sprinkle it on salads and vegetables. It's often found in the bulk section or in the baking aisle near the flours of the grocery store.

Zesty Ranch Seasoning Blend

Yields 4 tablespoons

Ingredients:

2 tablespoons dry buttermilk powder
  (if using regular dry milk, add ¼ teaspoon citric acid)
2 teaspoons dried parsley
1 teaspoon onion powder
1 teaspoon garlic powder
1 teaspoon dried chives
½ teaspoon dried dill
½ teaspoon freshly ground black pepper

Method:

1. Combine all ingredients in an airtight container. Shake well.

2. Store at room temperature, out of direct sunlight.

Helpful Tips:

Add this spice blend to a cup of sour cream or Greek yogurt to make your own homemade ranch dressing.

Dry buttermilk powder can usually be found in the baking aisle.

Italian Seasoning Blend

Yields ½ cup

Ingredients:

2 tablespoons dried oregano
1½ tablespoons dried basil
1½ tablespoons dried marjoram
1 tablespoon dried thyme
2 teaspoons dried rosemary
2 teaspoons dried sage
1 teaspoon garlic powder
1 teaspoon onion powder

Method:

1. Combine all ingredients in an airtight container. Shake well.

2. Store at room temperature, out of direct sunlight.

Helpful Tips:

To make into a paste, add 1 part spice mixture to 2 parts olive oil. Mix well. Serve as a dipping oil for bread.

Garam Masala Blend

Yields ¼ cup

Ingredients:

1 dried chili pepper, stems removed
  (chile de arbol, cayenne, Thai)
1 tablespoon cumin seeds
1 tablespoon coriander seeds
4 whole cardamom pods
1 teaspoon black peppercorns
2 whole cloves
cinnamon stick, broken into ½-inch pieces
¼ teaspoon ground nutmeg

Method:

1. Heat a large cast iron pan over medium heat.

2. Add dried pepper, cumin, coriander, cardamom pods, peppercorns, cloves, cinnamon, and nutmeg and dry roast (stirring frequently) until fragrant (about 2–3 minutes).

3. Remove from heat and let cool completely.

4. Transfer pepper mixture to a spice grinder and pulse until completely milled.

5. Transfer mixture to an airtight container and store at room temperature, out of direct sunlight.

Grilling Seasoning Blend

Yields ½ cup

Ingredients:

2 tablespoons dried oregano

1 tablespoon dried parsley

1 tablespoon dried thyme

1 tablespoon smoked paprika

1 tablespoon ancho chili powder

2 teaspoons granulated sugar

1 teaspoon garlic powder

1 teaspoon onion powder

1 teaspoon cumin

½ teaspoon freshly ground black pepper

½ teaspoon ground mustard

¼ teaspoon ground cinnamon

¼ teaspoon citric acid (see note below)

Method:

1. Combine all ingredients in an airtight container. Shake well.

2. Store at room temperature, out of direct sunlight.

Helpful Tips:

Citric acid is found naturally in lemons and limes and gives any seasoning blend a slightly tart/acidic punch. It counteracts the bitterness and complements the other flavors in the blend by rounding them out.

Southwest Spice Blend

Yields ½ cup

Ingredients:

2 tablespoons ancho chili powder

2 tablespoons smoked paprika

1 tablespoon dried oregano

2 teaspoons cumin

2 teaspoons garlic powder

2 teaspoons onion powder

1 teaspoon ground coriander

1 teaspoon cayenne pepper

½ teaspoon freshly ground black pepper

½ teaspoon citric acid

Method:

1. Combine all ingredients in an airtight container. Shake well.

2. Store at room temperature, out of direct sunlight.

Harissa Spice Blend

Yields ½ cup

Ingredients:

2 dried chilis, stems removed (chile de arbol, cayenne, Thai)

1 tablespoon cumin seeds

1 tablespoon coriander seeds

4 green cardamom pods

1 teaspoon black peppercorns

2 whole cloves

1½-inch cinnamon stick, broken into pieces

¼ teaspoon ground nutmeg

Method:

1. Heat a large cast iron pan over medium heat.

2. Add dried chilis, cumin, coriander, green cardamom pods, peppercorns, cloves, cinnamon and nutmeg and dry roast (stirring frequently) until fragrant (about 2–3 minutes).

3. Remove from the heat and let cool completely.

4. Transfer the pepper mixture to a spice grinder and pulse until completely milled.

5. Transfer the mixture to an airtight container and store at room temperature, out of direct sunlight.

Helpful Tips:

The variety of peppers will determine the heat and smokiness of the spice mixture.

How to Dry Herbs:

1. Preheat the oven to its lowest setting (about 200°), and line a baking pan with parchment paper.

2. Place fresh herbs in a colander and gently wash under cool, running water. Pat dry and remove leaves from the stems.

3. Spread the herb leaves evenly on the pan. Transfer to the oven and dry for about 30 minutes. When herbs are dry, remove them from the oven and let them cool completely.

4. Transfer the herbs to a spice grinder and pulse until desired consistency.

Microwave Method:

1. Lay clean herbs on a microwave plate or paper towels. Microwave for 30 second intervals, turning leaves over each time. Repeat until the leaves are dry and brittle, 2–3 minutes total.

Sauces
Pestos
Dressings

What differentiates an average meal from a great meal?

A good sauce or dressing. Sauces and dressings bring a dish together by complementing and enhancing flavors. Combine oil and vinegar with spices and herbs to create a tasty salad dressing or a light marinade for a protein like chicken or tofu. If your pasta or roasted vegetables need some extra flavor, opt for a pesto! Classic pesto is created by blending together basil, pine nuts, Parmesan cheese and olive oil — but pesto can also be created with other greens, tomatoes, nuts and cheeses, so experiment with what you have on hand and find flavor combinations you love. When you make sauces and dressings at home, you can customize the ingredients to your preferences. Make a hot sauce less spicy by choosing a mild pepper or by removing more of the pepper's seeds and white pith. Make a lighter, but still creamy, salad dressing by substituting plain yogurt in place of mayonnaise. Looking to reduce your salt intake? Omit salt from your dressings and sauces and add extra spices and herbs to amplify a recipe's flavors. Take your weeknight dinner from good to great by adding a homemade sauce or dressing.

Tomato Sauce

Yields 8 cups

Ingredients:

2 pounds of tomatoes, cut in half (Roma, garden, etc.)

2 carrots, cut into half moons

1 onion, thinly sliced

6 garlic cloves, peeled

2 tablespoons olive oil

1 teaspoon kosher salt

½ teaspoon freshly ground black pepper

8–10 fresh oregano stems, tied together with twine

8 cups water

Method:

1. Roasted tomatoes: Preheat the oven to 400° and line a large baking pan with parchment paper. Place tomatoes, carrots, onions and garlic on the pan and drizzle evenly with olive oil. Season with salt and pepper. Roast in the oven for 30–35 minutes until tomatoes are lightly browned and tender.

2. Sauce: Remove tomatoes and vegetables from the oven, transfer to a large soup pot and add oregano. Cover tomatoes and vegetables with water and bring the mixture to a boil over medium heat. Reduce the heat to low and continue cooking until the vegetables are soft, about 20–25 minutes. Discard the oregano and remove the tomato sauce from the heat. Let cool. Using an immersion blender, blend the mixture until it is smooth.

Helpful Tips:

Store tomato sauce in an airtight container in the refrigerator and use within a week or in the freezer for up to 3 months.

Helpful tips for pesto:

1. Pesto can be made with a variety of herbs and plants, such as basil, parsley, kale, arugula or carrot tops.

2. Any soft nut can replace the traditional pine nuts such as walnuts or pecans.

3. Cheese can be replaced with nutritional yeast for a vegan option.

4. Pesto can be thinned using water or vegetable broth.

Carrot Top Pesto

Yields 1 cup

Ingredients:

2 cups carrot top greens

½ cup fresh basil

⅓ cup unsalted walnuts, roasted

4 garlic cloves, peeled

1 lemon, juiced (about 2 tablespoons)

¼ cup grated Parmigiano Reggiano cheese

1 tablespoon tomato paste

¼ teaspoon kosher salt

¼ teaspoon freshly ground black pepper

½ cup extra virgin olive oil

1–2 tablespoons water for thinning, as needed

Method:

1. In a food processor, add carrot greens, basil, walnuts, garlic and lemon juice and pulse until finely chopped but not smooth.

2. Add cheese, tomato paste, salt and black pepper and pulse until well blended. Slowly add olive oil while pulsing until combined but not pureed. Add water to adjust consistency, if needed.

3. Transfer to an airtight container and store in the refrigerator for up to 1 week.

Walnut Basil Pesto

Yields about 1 cup

Ingredients:

4 cups fresh basil (Genovese, lemon or spicy globe)

⅓ cup unsalted walnuts, roasted

4 garlic cloves, peeled

1 lemon, zest and juice (about 2 tablespoons juice)

¼ cup grated Parmigiano Reggiano cheese

½ cup olive oil

kosher salt to taste

freshly ground black pepper to taste

1–2 tablespoons water for thinning, as needed

Method:

1. In a food processor, add all ingredients except water and pulse until smooth. Taste and adjust seasoning. Add water to adjust consistency, if needed.

2. Spoon into an airtight container, cover with a piece of plastic wrap to prevent browning and put the lid on tightly. Store in the refrigerator for up to 1 week.

Fresh Cranberry and Orange Relish

Serves 4–6

Ingredients:

¼ cup pitted dates (about 5)

1 tablespoon canola or vegetable oil

¼ cup fresh orange juice

1 cup fresh cranberries, washed

2 navel oranges, peeled

1 sweet apple, core removed and chopped

½ cup unsalted walnuts, toasted and chopped

¼ teaspoon ground cinnamon

Method:

1. In a food processor, combine dates, oil and orange juice and pulse until the mixture is smooth. Add cranberries, oranges, apples, walnuts and cinnamon and pulse until the mixture resembles a rough chopped relish (do not over-pulse).

2. Store in an airtight container in the refrigerator for 2–3 days.

Sweet Pepper Vinaigrette

Yields about ½ cup

Ingredients:

1 teaspoon plus 4 tablespoons canola oil

½ cup baby sweet bell peppers
  (red, yellow or orange), thinly sliced

1 shallot, thinly sliced

1 garlic clove, thinly sliced

2 tablespoons sherry vinegar

3–4 sprigs fresh thyme, stems removed

1 teaspoon honey

pinch of kosher salt

Method:

1. In a small saucepan, heat 1 teaspoon of oil until hot and shimmery.

2. Add bell peppers and cook, stirring frequently until fragrant, about 1 minute. Add shallots and garlic. Sauté until lightly browned, about 2–3 minutes.

3. Transfer the pepper mixture to a blender or food processor. Add 4 tablespoons of oil and the remaining ingredients and blend until smooth.

4. Store in an airtight container in the refrigerator for up to 1 week.

Tomatillo and Avocado Salsa

Yields 4 cups

Ingredients:

8–10 tomatillos, husks removed

1 avocado, peeled and seeded

½ white onion, peeled

1 jalapeño, stem removed

2 garlic cloves, peeled

1 lime, juiced

½ teaspoon cumin

½ teaspoon kosher salt

¼ bunch fresh cilantro

Method:

1. In a blender or food processor, add all ingredients except cilantro and blend until smooth. Add cilantro and pulse. Taste and adjust seasonings.

2. To prevent browning of the salsa, cover tightly with plastic wrap and store in an airtight container for 2–3 days in the refrigerator.

Creamy Chimichurri

Yields 1 cup

Ingredients:

2 small mandarin oranges, peeled

2 garlic cloves, peeled

¼ bunch fresh parsley, chopped (about ½ cup)

¼ bunch fresh cilantro, chopped (about ½ cup)

1 serrano pepper, stem removed

1 avocado, peeled and seeded

1 tablespoon olive oil

1 tablespoon apple cider vinegar

½ teaspoon kosher salt

Method:

1. In a blender or food processor, combine all ingredients. Blend until smooth.

2. Store in an airtight container in the refrigerator for up to 1 week.

Helpful Tips:

To increase the vegetable protein, add toasted nuts.

Greek yogurt can be substituted for the avocado.

If the sauce needs to be thinned, add a few extra orange slices.

Smokey Poblano Hot Sauce

Yields about 1 cup

Ingredients:

5 fresh poblano peppers, stems removed, seeded (about 1 pound)

1 tablespoon canola oil

1 sweet onion, quartered

3 garlic cloves, peeled

1 cup water

½ cup white vinegar

1 teaspoon smoked paprika

1 teaspoon kosher salt

Method:

1. Preheat the oven to broil and line a baking pan with foil. Spread poblano peppers, onion and garlic evenly on the pan, making sure not to overcrowd. Drizzle with canola oil. Roast in the oven for 5 minutes on each side until poblano peppers are charred.

2. Heat a medium-sized pot over medium-high heat and add roasted peppers, onions, garlic, water, vinegar, smoked paprika and salt and bring to a boil. Reduce heat and simmer for 3–5 minutes or until the poblanos are soft.

3. Transfer the pepper mixture in batches to a blender or food processor and blend until smooth.

4. Pour the hot sauce into sterilized containers, let cool and store in the refrigerator for up to 3 months.

Hatch Chili Cream

Yields ½ cup

Ingredients:

3–4 hatch chilis

1 tablespoon olive oil

3 garlic cloves, peeled

¼ cup fat-free Greek yogurt

½ avocado, peeled and seeded

1 lime, juiced

¼ teaspoon kosher salt

Method:

1. Preheat broiler. Place chilis on a baking pan and drizzle with olive oil. Cook under broiler about 2–3 minutes on each side until peppers are evenly blistered.

2. Place peppers in a bowl and cover tightly with plastic wrap. Let sit for about 5 minutes. Discard stems.

3. In a blender or food processor, add all ingredients and blend until smooth.

4. Store in an airtight container in the refrigerator for up to 1 week.

Helpful Tips:

Hatch chilis are only available fresh during a few weeks in the late summer, but they usually can be found canned in the grocery store.

Substitute 4 ounces canned hatched chilis for 3–4 fresh hatch chilis.

Green Jalapeño Hot Sauce

Yields about 3 cups

Ingredients:

1 tablespoon canola oil

5–8 jalapeños, seeded and stems removed

½ sweet onion, diced

3 garlic cloves, minced

2 cups water

½ cup white vinegar

½ bunch fresh cilantro, stems removed

1 teaspoon kosher salt

Method:

1. In a medium-sized saucepan over medium-high heat, warm oil until hot and shimmery. Add jalapeños, onion and garlic and sauté until lightly browned, about 2–3 minutes. Add water, vinegar, cilantro and salt and bring to a boil. Reduce heat and simmer for 5–8 minutes or until the jalapeños are soft.

2. Transfer the pepper mixture to a blender or food processor and blend until smooth.

3. Pour the hot sauce into sterilized containers, let cool and store in the refrigerator for up to 3 months.

Nuts

Nuts are a category of nutrient-packed legumes (like peanuts) and seeds (like pecans, walnuts and pine nuts).

Nuts provide protein, unsaturated fats, vitamins and minerals and add a great textural contrast to many dishes, like salads and pastas. When deciding between raw, salted or roasted nuts for your next snack or recipe, the main difference is flavor. Roasting nuts at high temperatures creates a richer taste.

Candied Nuts

Yields about 3 cups

Ingredients:

3 tablespoons unsalted butter

¼ cup brown sugar

2 tablespoons honey

¼ teaspoon kosher salt

3 cups pecan halves (or other nuts)

Method:

1. Preheat the oven to 375° and line a baking pan with parchment paper.

2. In a large cast iron pan over medium heat, add the butter, brown sugar, honey and salt and stir constantly, cooking until mixture is bubbly, about 3–4 minutes. Stir in pecans and continue cooking until the mixture is thickened and coats the pecans, about 2–3 minutes.

3. Spread the pecan mixture evenly on the pan, making sure not to overcrowd. Roast pecans in the oven until fragrant and evenly browned, about 6–8 minutes. Remove, let cool and store in an airtight container out of the sunlight.

Spiced Mixed Nuts

Yields about 3 cups

Ingredients:

¼ cup date sugar

2 teaspoons berbere spice (or spice blend of choice)

¼ teaspoon kosher salt

1 egg white

1 cup whole Marcona almonds (or other nuts)

1 cup shelled pistachios (or other nuts)

1 cup whole cashews (or other nuts)

Method:

1. Preheat the oven to 300° and line a baking pan with parchment paper.

2. In a small bowl, mix together sugar, berbere spice and salt. Set aside.

3. In a large bowl, whisk egg white until fluffy. Add almonds, pistachios, cashews and spice mixture and stir to evenly coat.

4. Spread the nut mixture on the baking pan, making sure not to overcrowd. Roast the nuts in the oven until fragrant and evenly browned, about 15–20 minutes. Remove, let cool and store in an airtight container out of the sunlight.

Sweet and Spicy Nuts

Yields about 3 cups

Ingredients:

3 tablespoons olive oil

1 tablespoon finely chopped fresh rosemary leaves

2 tablespoons brown sugar

2 tablespoons maple syrup

1 tablespoon smoked paprika

½ teaspoon cayenne pepper

¼ teaspoon kosher salt

3 cups walnut halves (or other nuts)

Method:

1. Preheat the oven to 375° and line a baking pan with parchment paper.

2. In a large cast iron pan over medium heat, add olive oil, rosemary, brown sugar, maple syrup, smoked paprika, cayenne pepper and salt. Stir constantly until mixture is bubbly, about 3–4 minutes. Stir in walnuts and continue cooking until the mixture has thickened and coats the walnuts, about 2–3 minutes.

3. Spread the walnut mixture evenly on the baking pan, making sure not to overcrowd. Roast in the oven until fragrant and evenly browned, about 6–8 minutes. Remove, let cool and store in an airtight container out of the sunlight.

Helpful Hints:

Nuts can be stored in an airtight container in the refrigerator for up to 6 months or in the freezer for a year.

Try toasting nuts two ways:

1. Place nuts in a 300° oven on a baking sheet lined with parchment paper for no longer than 15 minutes.

2. Place nuts in a skillet over medium-low heat until they produce a nutty aroma, shaking the pan every minute or so.

It's best to roast nuts whole so they brown at the same rate.

Buy nuts in bulk. They are typically fresher.

To make homemade nut milk:

Soak 1 cup raw cashews or raw almonds for 4 hours or overnight in an airtight container and rinse until the water is clear. The water can be a 4:1 or 5:1 water to nut ratio. Blend on high in a high-powered blender with water until creamy. Use 1, 2 or 3 cups of water — the less water the creamier the milk. Stir in sweetener of choice and flavorings. Almonds need to be strained in a nut bag before adding sweeteners.

Oils

The many varieties of oils may feel overwhelming, but the differences among them are simpler than you think! Oils are usually classified based on flavor profile and smoke point. The smoke point of an oil is the temperature at which the oil begins to break down and produce smoke — this often will give food a bitter and burnt flavor. Olive oil has a very distinct flavor and a lower smoke point (between 390° and 465°), making it perfect for roasting vegetables or serving with a crusty baguette. Extra virgin olive oil has an even lower smoke point (between 350° and 410°) which makes it best to use for cold preparations like dressings. Other oils good for roasting are canola and avocado oil, both of which have a neutral flavor and higher smoke point (around 425°–475˚). They are also good for roasting and great for high-heat cooking methods like sautéing, stir frying and pan frying. You can add more flavor to oils by infusing them with ingredients like herbs and garlic. Drizzling a small amount of herb-infused oil over the top of roasted vegetables gives them extra moisture and flavor.

Green Herb Oil
Yields 1 cup

Ingredients:

2 quarts water
½ bunch fresh parsley (about 1 cup with stems)
½ bunch fresh basil (about ½ cup with stems)
1 bunch fresh chives (about ½ cup)
1 cup olive oil

Method:

1. Blanch and shock: Create an ice bath by placing ice in a large bowl and covering with water. Set aside. In a medium pot over high heat, bring 2 quarts of water to a boil. Reduce the heat to a simmer and add herbs. Cook until wilted, about 20–30 seconds. Using a slotted spoon, transfer immediately to the ice bath to let cool. Drain herbs using a strainer and place in a lint-free towel and squeeze to remove as much water as possible.

2. Herb oil: Transfer the blanched herbs to a blender or food processor and add oil and blend until very smooth, about 1–2 minutes. Line a fine mesh strainer with cheesecloth and set the strainer over a small pot or bowl. Slowly pour the pureed oil mixture and let it funnel through the cloth. Transfer the oil to a sterilized jar and store in the refrigerator for up to 3 months.

Turmeric and Ginger Oil
Yields 1 cup

Ingredients:

1 cup olive oil
2 tablespoons turmeric, peeled and grated (about 2 inches)
2 tablespoons grated fresh ginger, peeled (about 2 inches)

Method:

1. In a medium pot over medium heat, warm the oil, turmeric and ginger to 180°, stirring frequently. Remove from the heat and let cool to room temperature, about 1 hour.

2. In a blender or food processor, add the turmeric mixture and blend until very smooth, about 1–2 minutes.

3. Line a fine mesh strainer with cheesecloth and set the strainer over a small pot or bowl. Slowly pour the pureed oil mixture and let it funnel through the cloth. Transfer the oil to a sterilized jar and store in the refrigerator for up to 3 months.

Oregano, Thyme, Rosemary and Garlic Oil
Yields 1 cup

Ingredients:

½ bunch fresh oregano, washed and dried (about 1 cup with stems)
1 bunch fresh thyme, washed and dried (about ½ cup with stems)
1 bunch fresh rosemary, washed and dried (about ½ cup with stems removed)
6 garlic cloves, peeled and crushed
1 cup olive oil

Method:

1. In a medium pot over low heat, warm all the ingredients to 180°, stirring frequently. Remove from the heat and let cool to room temperature, about 1 hour.

2. Transfer the oil mixture to a blender or a food processor and blend until very smooth, about 1–2 minutes.

3. Line a fine mesh strainer with cheesecloth and set the strainer over a small pot or bowl. Slowly pour the pureed oil mixture and let it funnel through the cloth. Transfer the oil to a sterilized jar and store in the refrigerator for up to 3 months.

Helpful Tips:

Use a ratio of 2 parts herbs to 1 part oil, which equals 2 cups of packed basil to 1 cup of oil. This does not have to be exact — the more herbs, the more flavor.

Don't worry about removing stems; they can be strained out after.

Use a single herb or a mixture for different flavors.

Blanching and shocking the herbs brings out the bright green color.

If you don't have cheesecloth, a coffee filter will work.

Be careful: turmeric and ginger oil will stain.

Broths

A broth is a savory liquid that can be used as the base for soups and stews or as a replacement for water when making rice and other grains.

While there are not any official standards differentiating between broth and stock, traditionally stock is prepared by simmering bones and vegetables in water, while broth is made with meat and/or vegetables. The collagen present in the bones causes stock to be thicker than broth. Just because broth is not thick does not mean it isn't flavorful. Spices, along with vegetable and meat scraps, give broth a craveable umami flavor. Freeze your broth in an ice cube tray or a zipper-lock bag for easy storage and access when you want to add a little flavor to homemade recipes.

Umami Mushroom Broth

Yields 8 cups

Ingredients:

8 cups water

1 ounce dried mushrooms (shiitake), placed in a cheesecloth bag

1 pound of mixed vegetables, thinly sliced

4 sheets of seaweed

1-inch ginger root, thinly sliced

1-inch turmeric root, thinly sliced

4 garlic cloves, peeled and crushed

1 teaspoon kosher salt

½ teaspoon black peppercorns

2 tablespoons white miso paste

Method:

1. In a large pot over medium heat, add water, cheesecloth bag with mushrooms, vegetables, seaweed sheets, ginger, turmeric, garlic, salt and peppercorns. Bring to a boil then reduce the heat to low and continue cooking until the vegetables are soft, about 30–35 minutes.

2. Remove from the heat, strain out the vegetables, seaweed, turmeric, garlic and peppercorns, leaving the broth in the pot. Whisk in miso paste, return the mushroom bag and continue cooking over low heat for an additional 15 minutes.

3. Remove from the heat and let cool.

4. When completely cool, store in the refrigerator in an airtight container for 4–5 days or in the freezer for up to 4 months.

Vegetable Broth

Yields 8 cups

Ingredients:

8 cups water

2 pounds of mixed vegetables (onions, celery, carrots, etc.)

2 tablespoons chopped fresh herbs (thyme, parsley, etc.)
  or 1 tablespoon Italian Seasoning Blend (see recipe page 253)

1 teaspoon kosher salt

½ teaspoon freshly ground black pepper

Method:

1. In a large pot over medium heat, bring 8 cups of water, the vegetables, fresh herbs, salt and pepper to a boil. Make sure the vegetables are covered by the water. Bring to a boil, then lower the heat to a simmer and continue cooking until the vegetables are soft, about 45 minutes.

2. Remove from the heat. Using a fine mesh strainer, strain the broth and vegetables over a large bowl and discard the cooked vegetables. Let the broth cool and then store in the refrigerator in an airtight container for 4–5 days or in the freezer for up to 4 months.

Helpful Tips:

Traditional broth uses mirepoix: 2 parts onion, 1 part carrot and 1 part celery.

Avoid strong-flavored vegetables like Brussels sprouts or cabbage.

Add immune-boosting ingredients such as spices and flavor enhancers such as lemon, turmeric, ginger, garlic and miso.

Hearty soups start with broths such as vegetable, chicken or beef and then vegetables, whole grains, seasonings, herbs and citrus are added for a bright touch.

HOW GOOD FOOD WORKS IN YOUR LIFE

DOLORES WOODS

MA, RDN, LD
NUTRITIONIST SUPERVISOR

> "The key is to help people understand that maintaining a good diet doesn't have to be complicated or take a lot of time," she continued. "If we can make it easy as well as flavorful — using fresh, seasonal products, the right ingredients, herbs and spices — they'll do it."

It took five years, but Dolores Woods finally had enough.

After graduating from the University of California at Riverside and going straight to the French Cooking Institute, she began to chase her dream of eventually owning a restaurant. But the hours were long, and she got tired of working nights and holidays. "I didn't love it enough," she said.

But what Woods — the community outreach specialist and a full time instructor in culinary medicine for the Nourish program — later discovered was that she loved healthy eating. When a friend of her sister's planted the idea that she become a dietitian, Woods enrolled in the master's program in food studies at New York University, followed by a coordinated dietetics program in Los Angeles to get her credentials.

It was there, after finishing her studies, that Woods' new career began to take shape.

"I was with a Head Start program in LA, training kids from kindergarten to age five how to eat healthy," she said. "People were saying, 'Ugh, they're too young, they won't eat any of that.' But they did."

She faced the same kind of skepticism in her next job, nutrition coordinator at UCLA, where she was involved in opening the first healthy-eating dining hall in the country. "We kept hearing people say no one would come," Woods said. "It turned out to be a huge success."

"There was just shock and amazement that all of this worked. It shows that if you make food taste good, people will eat it."

Next up was the University of Houston as Director of Wellness and Sustainability, with responsibilities that included providing nutrition education and training support to dining services associates, staff and faculty.

But it was Nourish, which she joined in October 2020, that gave Woods an opportunity to put all of her education and work experience to the fullest possible use.

At NYU, her studies concentrated on cultural and environmental approaches to food. "We were taught that food was the lens through which we view the world," she explained. It was a good fit with Nourish's focus on the societal benefits of healthy eating and preparing students to take the good nutrition message into communities.

"What I love about doing what I do is helping and mentoring students who are committed to making lives better," she said. "Our goal is to develop future dieticians with the skill-sets they need to improve the health and lifestyles of people by showing them how good food works for them and their families.

"Making it simple," Woods added, "is an important part of that process."

JEANNE PIGA-PLUNKETT

MS, RDN, LD
FACULTY ASSOCIATE / DIRECTOR OF DIETETIC INTERNSHIP

Jeanne Piga-Plunkett got an up-close-and-personal look at how good food is linked to good health.

Her grandmother was diabetic, which at the time was something Piga-Plunkett, then in the fourth grade, didn't entirely understand. But as she got older, she began to notice something.

"My grandmother had been to a dietitian, who made some suggestions on how she could eat healthier," said Piga-Plunkett, director of the dietetic internship program at the University of Texas Health Science Center and a member of the Nourish faculty. "And it became apparent to me that she did better when she ate well. The connection was really clear."

A few years later, it became even clearer.

Piga-Plunkett began playing sports as a ninth-grader and quickly advanced to junior varsity and then varsity, working out, losing weight, and "becoming very fit." That's when she saw the connection again.

"I started to realize that food was tied to exercise and performance," she explained. "When I got to college as a tennis player, I understood that the better my eating habits, the better I was on the court."

That realization set her on a decades-long path that brought her to UTHealth.

The first stop was at a long-term care facility. "All the complaints were about the food," Piga-Plunkett recalled, "and they were right. It didn't look good or taste good, and it wasn't presented well. It just wasn't very interesting." She fixed that and, as was the case with her grandmother, saw the relationship between recovery and improved health. "I learned how good food works."

From there, she went on to food services in a children's psychiatric facility. "These kids were abandoned, neglected and abused," she continued, "and had a lot of issues, as you can imagine. My job was to make sure food wasn't one of them — and to make food fun." She paused and laughed. "Needless to say, we didn't serve liver."

She then took a job with a private high school where the food was "just horrible." For example, "They'd take a quarter head of lettuce, chop it up, toss it in a bowl, and call it a salad." She set out to fix that, too.

To begin with, Piga-Plunkett got the school baking its own bread, offering three entrees — one of them vegetarian — preparing nutritious soups, adding some carrots and fresh fruit into the salad, and creating a hamburger bar. Then something interesting happened.

"The freshmen were at the burger bar," she said. "But by October, they saw that the upperclassmen were lined up for the healthy food, so they did, too." The school dietitians would ask her how she managed to get the kids to eat vegetables. Her answer? "Make them taste better."

Piga-Plunkett was there for 17 years. "Every year, the food got better," she said, "and we became a model for how to do it right."

After taking a job heading food services for a program for the elderly in Princeton, N.J., where her husband was studying for the ministry, she returned to Houston, consulted for a year, then was the first director of Brighter Bites, a nonprofit that brings fruit and vegetables to families in underserved communities.

In 2014, in what she called a "natural progression," Piga-Plunkett joined UTHealth, where she teaches courses that include nutrition practices, public health and medical nutrition, and is an advisor for Nourish's holistic garden.

Piga-Plunkett, who earned her undergraduate degree in food science from the University of Texas at Austin and her master's in clinical nutrition from Texas Women's University, has found her experience since coming to Nourish to be rewarding on multiple levels.

"Building this program has been amazing," she said. "To have the opportunity to implement my ideas, and to be with people who are just so devoted to healthy eating, has been a gift."

Like her colleagues in Nourish, she finds working with students to be especially gratifying.

"Mentoring them is so much fun," Pia-Plunkett continued. "There's a lot to learn — things change every day — and it's wonderful to be with and around students. I get pleasure out of doing well, and I want them to do well, and to get them where they want to be."

"I guess I'm kind of like their cheerleader."

Acknowledgements

My husband, **Don Sanders**, you are an inspiration to all. You are an extremely generous and loving man who believed in me and my vision of teaching our community a healthier way of living. Thank you for standing by my side the entire way and for supporting Nourish not only as a viable organization but by providing the funding to help it grow into a successful train-the-trainer and community outreach program.

My family, **Ashley** and **Mike Batistick** and **Mallory** and **Diego Fernandez** — you are my world. Thank you for always supporting me over the years in all my endeavors and for being my cheerleaders and voices of reason. My love for you is unconditional.

Georgene Brandon — you were the spark that ignited this book — I could not have done it without you. Thank you for a friendship of almost 40 years.

Tanya Mears and **Carol Calderoni** — two friendships that have lasted a lifetime. Thank you for joining me on our trips to taste the delicious foods around the world and for listening to me talk endlessly about my healthy goals for our communities.

My friends, **Maria Rangel** and **Socorro Zavala,** for their many long hours assisting with the team at home — **Lucy, Emma Arlo, Kirby, Jack, Kate** and JJ, who are always waiting with smiles.

The Cookbook Team

Roni Atnipp (the quarterback) — the most knowledgeable, organized cookbook consultant, support system and friend. Overseeing every aspect of the project — you turned this book from an idea into a reality. Thank you!

Elise DeSilva — thank you for the countless hours on the production and your graphic artistry. Your expertise in the design of each and every page is truly a work of art. Your support in the process of making this book is truly appreciated.

Debra Smail — for capturing the beauty of food — your level of photographic artistry is truly amazing. Thank you to **Rene Sides** for always being there during photo shoots. Your willingness was certainly

noted when assisting with props or whatever was needed to make the perfect photo and deliver the best street tacos too!

Omar Pereney — an amazing culinarian — thank you for your endless patience and skill and for making our food look absolutely beautiful with assistance from Chef Carlos Serrano and Chef Chris Cai.

Doug Williams — for putting our thoughts and visions into words, making this a truly readable book — not just a cookbook.

Alexander and **Linda Rogers** — for amazing portraits. Thank you for all the hours spent in the garden, kitchen and simulation lab, capturing our faculty and students at what they do best.

The Nourish Team

Wesley McWhorter — I'm grateful you joined the team when you enrolled as a PhD student in behavioral health at the UTHealth School of Public Health. You are a passionate educator and you truly believe that food is medicine. You are our champion and lead for our evidence-based research and culinary medicine.

Jeanne Piga-Plunkett — my dear friend and colleague — I'd be lost without you. From the first days when it was just the two of us gardening, cooking and teaching — the program wouldn't be what it is today without your support, experience and true love of mentoring our interns.

Joe Novak — our resident gardener PhD — thank you for believing in the vision in the very beginning. Your holistic gardening expertise and garden design along with your patience when working with our students is true dedication!

Deanna Hoelscher — Dean of the Austin Regional Campus of UTHealth School of Public Health and my mentor. I'm grateful for your support of the Nourish Program and all my "big" ideas, your advice on how to navigate the academic system and last but not least your friendship. The road to making visionary ideas work in such a large system has had its challenges — I appreciate you standing by my side.

Shreela Sharma — it seems like forever ago when we had a casual conversation about building our garden, teaching kitchen and simulation lab for our students. Thank you for helping me work out the kinks and supporting new program ideas!

Dolores Woods — the newest member of the team — I'm so grateful you joined the team as a lecturer, chef and dietitian — thank you for sharing your culinary and nutrition expertise with our students and your many hours of recipe testing and recipe tweaking for the cookbook. Your passion for teaching is amazing!

Susie Day — a special friend and colleague — thank you for all your support of our program. I appreciate you sharing your 35 years of nutrition epidemiology expertise, guiding our students through the grant writing process and for taking the lead on our grants for our successful health and wellness classes.

Jessica Canez — an excellent videographer and editor of all our cooking videos. Many hours of recipe prep, filming and editing – so talented and patient! And to **Macy Diulus** — thank you for all your assistance in helping us create our visual record for all our recipes.

Aislinn O'Kelly — an amazing writer who researched our introductions and delivered facts in an interesting, informative and readable way.

Our program operation would not be possible without the following organizations and foundations:

Blue Cross Blue Shield of Texas — thank you for sharing our vision and supporting our mission to help communities learn to live healthier lives. Your generosity has allowed us to build a virtual nutrition toolkit and share that with clinics and communities around the world.

Vivian L Smith Foundation — thank you for allowing us to train future trainers as we move into new communities and share our culinary and nutrition education.

The Allen Foundation — our first grantor — allowed our team to move into community clinics and centers to teach patients and community members how to make healthy food taste good.

Annette and Andy Schatte — thank you for your very generous gifts dedicated towards our work in the community — helping families in our city and state live healthier lives.

Sue Smith — shared the belief that children can live healthier lives, which has allowed us to take our portable teaching kitchen and train in schools.

Saranne and **Livingston Kosberg** — long-time supporters of communities in need around the world. Nourish is very grateful for your support of our goal to assist communities in our city who need education in food literacy and nutrition.

From the very beginning, UTHealth School of Public Health was on board with the idea of Nourish training future public health students and healthcare professionals how to make healthy food taste good. I am very grateful to UTHealth president, **Giuseppe N. Colasurdo, MD** and the dean of UTHealth School of Public Health **Eric Boerwinkle, PhD** — both of whom have been huge supporters of our mission and continue to support our endeavors.

HOW GOOD FOOD WORKS

has added a virtual toolkit of culinary skills and recipe prep with the help of a QR code. If you are unsure of a cooking technique or how the recipe steps come together, our digital toolkit will show you how – step by step! Not sure how to prep an artichoke or rice cauliflower?

Check out the video!
With a simple click on your cell phone, your book becomes digital.

Scan this QR code with your cell phone camera to visit the Nourish video kitchen.

COOKBOOK SOURCES AND REFERENCES

BBC Travel. https://www.bbc.com/travel.

Bon Appetit. *https://www.bonappetit.com*

Cooking Light. https://www.cookinglight.com

Evergreen Seeds. https://www.evergreenseeds.com.

Extension at the University of Minnesota. https://extension.umn.edu.

Food Source Information: Colorado Integrated Food Safety Center of Excellence. https://fsi.colostate.edu/.

Herb Society of America. https://www.herbsociety.org.

History.com. https://www.history.com.

Kitchn. https://www.thekitchn.com.

López-Alt J. Kenji. *The Food Lab: Better Home Cooking through Science*. New York: W. W. Norton & Company; 2015.

Miller OAG, Miller G, Smith BH. Home & Garden Information Center | Clemson University, South Carolina. https://hgic.clemson.edu/

NY Food Museum. http://www.nyfoodmuseum.org.

The Old Farmer's Almanac. https://www.almanac.com.

Rahman MS. Allicin and Other Functional Active Components in Garlic: Health Benefits and Bioavailability. *International Journal of Food Properties*. 2007;10(2): 245-268. doi:10.1080/10942910601113327.

Rombauer IS, Becker MR, Becker E. *Joy of Cooking*. New York: Scribner; 2002.

Texas A&M AgriLife Extension Service. https://AgriLifeExtension.tamu.edu.

The Spruce Eats. https://www.thespruceeats.com.

UCHealth. https://www.uchealth.org.

USDA ARS. https://www.ars.usda.gov.

Wisconsin Department of Public Instruction. https://dpi.wi.gov.

Italics indicate illustrations.

UTHealth®

The University of Texas
Health Science Center at Houston

School of Public Health

If you would like to donate to support the Nourish program
in helping others live healthier lives, please scan this QR code.

All donations go directly to
our community programing.

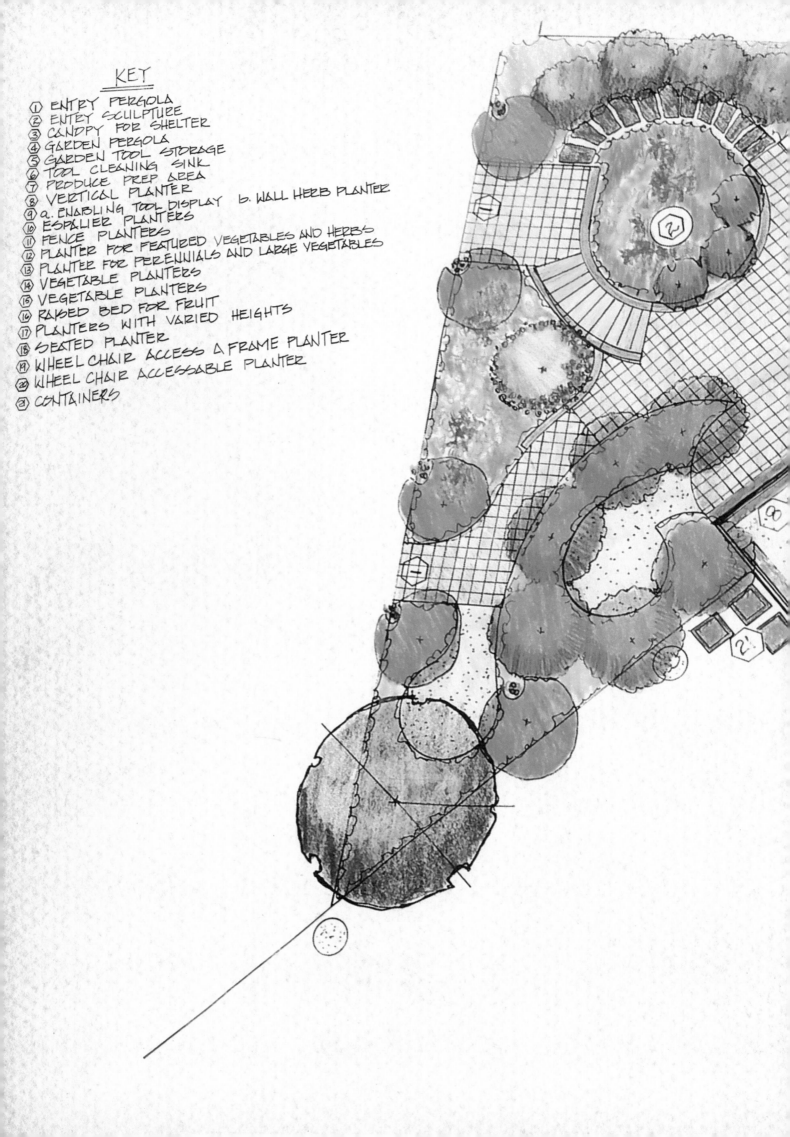

KEY
1. ENTRY PERGOLA
2. ENTRY SCULPTURE
3. CANOPY FOR SHELTER
4. GARDEN PERGOLA
5. GARDEN TOOL STORAGE
6. TOOL CLEANING SINK
7. PRODUCE PREP AREA
8. VERTICAL PLANTER
9. a. ENABLING TOOL DISPLAY   b. WALL HERB PLANTER
10. ESPALIER PLANTERS
11. FENCE PLANTERS
12. PLANTER FOR FEATURED VEGETABLES AND HERBS
13. PLANTER FOR PERENNIALS AND LARGE VEGETABLES
14. VEGETABLE PLANTERS
15. VEGETABLE PLANTERS
16. RAISED BED FOR FRUIT
17. PLANTERS WITH VARIED HEIGHTS
18. SEATED PLANTER
19. WHEELCHAIR ACCESS A FRAME PLANTER
20. WHEELCHAIR ACCESSABLE PLANTER
21. CONTAINERS